deaf worlds

INTERNATIONAL JOURNAL OF DEAF STUDIES

volume 22 issue 1 | 2006

SUBSCRIPTIONS

The international journal *DeafWorlds* is published three times per year.
For subscription information contact:

Douglas McLean
8 St John Street
Coleford
Gloucestershire GL16 8AR
England

www.ForestBooks.com
01594 833858 *text phone*
01594 833366 *voice phone*
01594 810637 *video phone*
01594 833446 *fax*

ISSN 1362–3125

Typeset in 12.5/15pt Perpetua
Printed and bound by The Cromwell Press,
Trowbridge, Wiltshire
Designed by Red Lizard Ltd.

EDITOR
Graham H. Turner *Heriot-Watt University, Edinburgh, Scotland*

EDITORIAL ASSISTANT
Jacqueline Meechan

ASSOCIATE EDITORS
Breda Carty *University of Newcastle, Australia*
Meike van Herreweghe *University of Ghent, Belgium*
Jens Hessmann *University of Magdeburg-Stendal, Germany*
Ben Karlin *Missouri Department of Mental Health, USA*
Lorraine Leeson *University of Dublin, Ireland*
Leila Monaghan *Indiana University, USA*
Carol Padden *University of California, USA*
Adam Schembri *University College, London, England*
Bencie Woll *University College, London, England*

EDITORIAL BOARD
Sangeeta Bagga-Gupta *Örebro University, Sweden*
Ben Bahan *Gallaudet University, USA*
Beppie van den Bogaerde *University of Amsterdam, the Netherlands*
Ann Darby *unaffiliated*
Kris Dekesel *University of Wolverhampton, England*
Susan Gregory *unaffiliated*
Peter Hindley *South West London and St. George's Mental Health NHS Trust, England*
Lesley Jones *Universities of York and Leeds, England*
Paddy Ladd *University of Bristol, England*
David McKee *Victoria University of Wellington, New Zealand*
Doug McLean *Forest Bookshop, England*
Pirkko Mikkonen *Humanities Polytechnic, Finland*
George Montgomery *Donaldson's College, Scotland*
David Moorhead *The Open University, UK*
Jemina Napier *Macquarie University, Australia*
Anna-Lena Nilsson *Stockholm University, Sweden*
Kyra Pollitt *University of Central Lancashire, England*
Jim Roots, *Canadian Association of the Deaf, Canada*
Cynthia Roy *Gallaudet University, USA*
Dierdre Schlehofer *University of Rochester, USA*
Constanze Schmaling *unaffiliated*
Richard Senghas *Sonoma State University, USA*
Ernst Thoutenhoofd *Royal Netherlands Academy of Arts and Sciences, the Netherlands*

EDITORIAL STATEMENT
The views expressed in Deaf Worlds may represent neither those of the editorial board or the editorial team, nor those of the publisher.

Articles that are relatively non-traditional will not be subject to academic refereeing procedures and this will be identified explicitly within the publication, including page numbers (by the prefix 'S').

AIMS AND SCOPE

DeafWorlds is the premier international journal of Deaf Studies, providing a focus for analysis and debate on social, cultural, historical, political, linguistic, anthropological and psychological factors influencing the lives of individual Deaf people, and their relationships with the communities and societies in which they live. The journal views Deaf people as a socially and culturally diverse group. Of particular importance in this context are multidisciplinary developments in scholarship, policy and provision, and advances in human and civil rights which aim to address the quality of Deaf people's lives.

DeafWorlds will publish original contributions set within any theoretical, epistemological or methodological framework, provided the material presented is rigorous, relevant and readable. Contributions must be submitted in English. Submission of an article will be taken to imply that it has not been published nor is being considered for publication elsewhere, either in its present form or in a modified version.

Whilst the bulk of each issue is expected to focus on relatively traditional scholarly journal articles, types of submission may also include:

• Additions to knowledge in the form of non-traditional research texts (including case studies)

• Short reports of work-in-progress

• Literature reviews and survey articles

• Conference reports

• Responses to articles previously published

• 'News from Xland' articles

• Squibs, i.e. shorter pieces which are specifically identified as 'exploratory', 'just a thought' or 'ideas in development', floating progressive possibilities for comment and feedback.

This volume is dedicated to
Deaf people living with and fighting
HIV/AIDS everywhere

Prologue

Deaf Worlds
2006 | vol 22 (1)
Forest Books ©
ISSN 1362–3125

Deaf people today are living with HIV and dying from AIDS at a far greater rate than their hearing counterparts. This has been obvious to people working with AIDS patients since the 1980s and has been public knowledge since the 1990s. David Van Biema wrote about the problem in Time Magazine in 1994,[1] the AIDS magazine POZ had a story on it in 1998,[2] and yet academic work on the subject or more recent general coverage is still scarce. No one even knows for sure how badly most Deaf communities have been affected because national and local health authorities rarely keep statistics on the issue. The figures from one exception to this trend, the Maryland Department of Public Health and Hygiene (United States), are terrifying – Deaf people tested in 2003 are twice as likely to be HIV+ as hearing people tested. When compared with rates of testing in the larger population, Deaf people in Maryland were ten times as likely as hearing people to be infected. Anecdotal evidence from Africa and Latin America paints an equally grim picture. Local communities, however, are fighting HIV/AIDS in a variety of creative ways. Activists in South Africa have developed AIDS education

---

1 Van Biema, D. (1994, April 4). AIDS and the Deaf. *Time Magazine, 143 (14),* 76-77.

2 POZ. (1998, April). Silence=Deaf. *POZ, 34.* Retrieved March 16, 2006, from
  http://www.poz.com/articles/226_1609.shtml

videotapes for South African students of all ages. In the Gambia, information about HIV is being spread in small training programmes and a play about the topic. In the Chicago area in the U.S., a group has developed a website with American Sign Languages videos on the topic.[3]

This *DeafWorlds* issue is our attempt to begin to rectify the lack of discussion of the problem in an academic forum. The unusually flexible format of this journal has allowed us to present academic articles, personal stories and even poetry and fiction on the extent of the problem and some of the solutions that communities in Africa, the United States and elsewhere have developed. We cast our net for contributors as widely as possible. We sent letters to every national Deaf association in the world, followed up every mention we could find on the internet, and asked colleagues working from South Africa to Brazil to Japan about the topic. Many thanks to all the people who responded, the material included here reflects the hard work of activists, public health officials and other researchers around the world. One of the things that we have been most pleased by is that asking questions about the impact of HIV/AIDS on Deaf communities has led to new research on the topic. Some of it is presented here, other work will be presented in a book we hope to publish as a follow up to this issue.

Even in a journal as flexible as *DeafWorlds*, the organization of this volume is unusual. As is typical, articles on pages with plain numbers are referreed, pieces on pages marked with 'S' are unreferreed. Usually the unreferreed section will come either at the beginning or the end of the volume. Here we present articles by region, divided into parts on Africa, the United States and elsewhere. Unrefereed material – personal stories, tributes and poetry – appears at the beginning of each of these sections, and is followed by reports from the field and refereed scholarly pieces. We feel that this balance between more artistic and more academic approaches to the topic gives a far better picture of the impact of HIV/AIDS than either approach alone would have. The personal story of John Meletse, the fiction of Ray Luczak, the survey work of Goldstein, Eckhardt, Joyner and Berry, the ethnographic work of Steven Fedorowicz and all the other pieces in this issue add up to a picture richer than

---

3 The website, a collaboration between Illinois Department of Public Health and the Deaf and Hard of Hearing Program at Advocate Illinois Masonic Behavior Health Services, can be found at http://www.advocatehealth.com/deaf.

a single piece would. We have included a map at the beginning that shows where the different authors come from or where their projects or research are located.

Many thanks to *Deaf Worlds,* including its editor Graham Turner, editorial assistant Jacqueline Meechan, layout director Roger Wyrill, and publisher Douglas McLean for their on-going and enthusiastic help and support. Not only is the format unusual, but the volume is also significantly longer than typical and will be more widely distributed. We are grateful for all their help in spreading the information contained in the volume on HIV/AIDS and Deafness. This work is only a beginning. We welcome contact with any other people willing to share their personal stories, community reports on the fight against HIV/AIDS, or scholarly articles on the issue.

Constanze Schmaling (Hamburg) and Leila Monaghan (Bloomington, Indiana)
constanze.schmaling@t-online.de and monaghan@indiana.edu
March, 2006

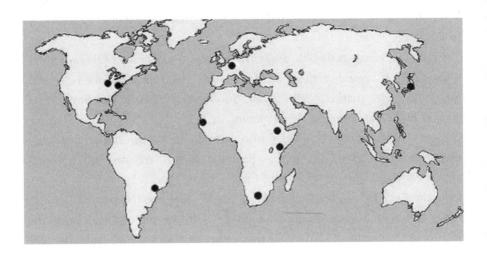

Contents

Deaf Worlds
2006 | vol 22 (1)
Forest Books ©
ISSN 1362–3125

HIV/AIDS and Deaf communities: An introduction

Amy Wilson and Leila Monaghan

Deaf Worlds
2006 | vol 22 (1)
Forest Books ©
ISSN 1362–3125

Key words

HIV/AIDS, deafness, international deaf issues, disease, developing countries, peer information networks

Abstract

There is an international HIV/AIDS epidemic affecting Deaf communities in every part of the globe. Few statistics exist on the extent of the problem but one study on Maryland (U.S.) infection rates shows that Deaf people are two to ten times as likely as their hearing counterparts to be HIV+. This article reviews the problems Deaf people have including poor access to information about HIV/AIDS and safe sex, inadequate treatment programs, and issues such as confidentiality in the community. We also suggest that Deaf empowerment and peer-to-peer information networks are the most powerful tools available for preventing the spread of HIV/AIDS and supporting Deaf people living with HIV. This article is an introduction to a Deaf Worlds issue on HIV/AIDS and Deafness and briefly previews many of the articles in the issue.

Biographies

Amy Wilson teaches graduate courses at Gallaudet University focusing on international development with people with disabilities in developing countries. She taught the sciences to Deaf high school students for twelve years and then volunteered four years with the Mennonite Central Committee doing development work with Deaf communities in northeast Brazil. Inspired by her experience in Brazil, she earned a Ph.D. at Gallaudet University's Department of Education (2001), focusing on curriculum development with an added specialization in International Development. She has conducted research in and with Deaf communities in Asia, the Caribbean, South America, Asia, and Africa. Dr. Wilson is interested in qualitative research methodologies which transform and empower traditionally marginalized groups, especially people with disabilities in the developing world.

Leila Monaghan is a linguistic anthropologist who teaches at Indiana University's Department of Communication and Culture. Her Ph.D. is from UCLA and she did her research with the New Zealand Deaf Community. She is the co-editor with Constanze Schmaling, Karen Nakamura and Graham H. Turner of *Many Ways to be Deaf: International Variation in Deaf Communities* and has articles in the *Annual Review of Anthropology* (with Richard Senghas) and the *Companion to Linguistic Anthropology* (with Barbara LeMaster) on the anthropology of Deaf communities and sign language variation. In addition to her continuing work on Deaf issues, she also does research on literacy and the teaching of interpersonal communication.

Introduction

More than 20 million men, women and children have died of AIDS since it was first recognized in 1981. Currently there are an estimated 48.5 million people infected worldwide (United Nations Population Fund, 2005). There are no recent figures on the number of Deaf people living in the world today, but in 1993 the World Federation of the Deaf estimated that there were 72 million Deaf people, of whom 54 million lived in developing countries (Mäkipää, 1993). It is unknown how many Deaf people have died of AIDS, or are currently infected with HIV, but it can be assumed for many reasons that their numbers are high and continue to grow. Leila Monaghan (this volume), reporting on 2003 statistics from Maryland in the United States, shows that Deaf people tested were on average more than twice as likely to be infected as the hearing people tested at the same sites. When these results are adjusted for Deaf population statistics, Deaf people were found to be over ten times more likely to be HIV+ than the population at large. While it is inappropriate to extrapolate from this limited American sample, the vulnerability of many Deaf people internationally suggests that not only are HIV infections and AIDS problems in Deaf communities, but that Deaf people are more susceptible to contracting HIV/AIDS than their hearing counterparts. This issue of Deaf Worlds focuses on describing the problem of HIV/AIDS among Deaf people both qualitatively (including autobiographical accounts of experiences, fiction and poetry) and quantitatively, and documenting some of the strategies that have been used around the world to combat the spread of AIDS and provide services to affected Deaf community members.

Issues of access to information

In general, people with disabilities have little chance of receiving special services or information about HIV/AIDS prevention or safe sex since less than 2% of all disabled children attend school (Scofield & Fineberg, 2002; Peters, 2003). In Deaf communities the lack of information is a particular problem. For example, Kenyan Deaf men uninformed about AIDS have been married by their communities to widows infected with HIV by their deceased husbands (Wilson & Kakiri, 2005). Print magazines and journals may not reach rural areas where a high rate of HIV exists, and the significant incidence of illiteracy or semi-illiteracy among Deaf people would hinder efforts to raise their awareness of HIV/AIDS through print. Radio programs teaching about HIV/AIDS are inaccessible to Deaf people and television programs are rarely interpreted or captioned. Recently, *Voice of America – Africa* telecast a four-minute story about HIV and Deaf women in Africa that aired throughout the continent. Despite the fact that the topic was about Deaf people, the show was neither interpreted nor captioned. Sex education programs targeted specifically for people with disabilities are rare (Robertson, Bhate & Bhate, 1991; Gaskins, 1999; Collins, Geller, Miller, Toro & Susser, 2001; UNAIDS, 2002).

The programs documented in this Deaf Worlds issue are important exceptions to this trend of inaccessible information. This issue's articles show that Deaf people themselves are the most promising weapons in the fight against HIV/AIDS in Deaf communities. In Kenya,

> the Kenya National Association of the Deaf (KNAD) realized that many deaf people were dying of AIDS. Even though the government, through the National Aids Control Council, boosted its HIV/AIDS awareness efforts aimed at behavior and attitude change through the media, such as radio, television, this information did not reach the deaf community. This is due to the fact that these information campaigns use spoken and written language which is difficult for Deaf people to access (Adoyo, this volume, p. S52).

In order to make HIV/AIDS information available to the Deaf community, ten Deaf youth attended a week of intensive training in the Nyanza, Western and Rift Valley Regions (abbreviated Nyaweri) about "the symptoms, prevalence, methods of infection, and prevention of HIV/AIDS." Teaching methods included full access to communication through Kenyan Sign Language, and using visually-oriented materials such as videos and demonstrations by Deaf puppeteers. With the knowledge they learned, the Deaf youth, in turn, have done a number of trainings for Deaf communities and at Deaf schools raising awareness about HIV/AIDS. They have also offered their services at three voluntary testing and counseling (VCT) sites and a number of mobile VCT sites which were open to Deaf walk-in clients (Adoyo, this volume; Henderson, this volume).

The predominantly Deaf South African group, Sign Language Education and Development (SLED), has created a series of four videos with Deaf actors using South African Sign Language. The videos, accompanied by training manuals specifically developed for the South African Deaf Community, discuss issues concerning general health and HIV/AIDS and are age appropriate whether for Deaf children, youth, or adults (Maclons, this volume). The Gambian Association of Deaf and Hard of Hearing People (GADHOH) recently trained its staff about HIV/AIDS who then gave presentations on the issue at three sites. Concurrently, 17 Deaf community members were recruited to do a play about HIV and AIDS that was presented at two sites (Schmaling & Loum, this volume).

Similar peer-to-peer techniques were also used successfully in Latin America. "Multiplying agents" were trained in Brazil to visit places frequented by Deaf people, such as public squares, bars, Deaf sports events, and the beach. The "multiplying agents" would pass out condoms, offer information about HIV/AIDS in an accessible format, and accompany people to testing sites if they wished (El Maerrawi, this volume). Outreach to Brazil's Gay Deaf community began in the 1990s. By 1995, AIDS had claimed the lives of two prominent community members, Roberto Robson and José Roberto Cruz. Norine Berenz (this volume) writes about how in the mid-1990s John McBride, a Gay American interpreter, circulated information about AIDS throughout the Gay Deaf community, including showing an explicit safe-sex video in American Sign Language.

Deaf communities in "developed nations," like the United States also have problems with access to information and education programs on HIV/AIDS (Sleek, 1994; Van Biema, 1994). Brad, a Deaf man living in New York with AIDS, for example, "feels certain that many of the deaf kids who are exposed to HIV haven't got a clue about the disease and the risks" (Poor, this volume, p. S76). The more formal studies of Goldstein, Eckhardt, Joyner and Berry (this volume), and Perlman and Leon (this volume) also show that Deaf people in the United States often lack the information that their hearing counterparts may possess. Even programs intended specifically for Deaf people may fail, such as the attempt to have an HIV/AIDS TTY phone information hotline in Flanders, Belgium (Heyerick, this volume). Countries where HIV infection is low, such as in Japan and the Czech Republic, reported there were no HIV programs for Deaf people. Steven Fedorowicz argues that in Japan the need for Deaf-centered programs is not recognized although infection rates might be higher in the Deaf population than in the general population (Fedorowicz, this volume).

Just as elsewhere, Deaf communities in the United States themselves provide solutions to some of the problems of HIV/AIDS. At Gallaudet University in the United States, Deaf college students are trained to be Peer Health Advocates (PHAs) where they teach their fellow students about safe sex, how to avoid HIV infection, and where to find health-related resources. The PHAs have developed informational skits and numerous humorous presentations, such as having "Condom Lady" run through the university cafeteria in order to save a student from someone dressed as an HIV virus (Roberts, this volume).

The treatment of Deaf HIV patients

Lack of awareness by professionals in the area of HIV/AIDS of the need to reach out to the Deaf community is a barrier to the design, implementation and evaluation of effective policy and programs throughout both the developed and developing world. The rarity of HIV/AIDS program components specifically designed for Deaf people, or the lack of programs which include them, may have equity implications in prevention and care, since they may be less likely than their hearing peers to receive counseling, support, or medical care when they begin to show symptoms of the disease. The story of John Meletse, the first openly HIV+ Deaf person in South Africa, is illustrative.

> I told the doctor that I needed an HIV test. They did not give me any counseling which is required in South Africa. The doctor did the test and told me to wait for 15 minutes outside until he could give me the results. I was very anxious. The doctor called me back and wrote on a piece of paper in large letters, "YOU ARE HIV POSITIVE". He put it in my face. I felt shocked and sick – I mouthed, "Is this true?" He nodded, "yes". He said "Goodbye you can go now" .... I walked home crying (Meletse & Morgan, this volume, p. S17).

When HIV/AIDS programs are provided to the Deaf community, they may not be presented in a way that the information can be easily understood, or with effective interpreting services. One Deaf community in an African nation was included in an HIV/AIDS workshop intended for health care professionals offered by a Northern development assistance organization. An interpreter was provided so that leaders in the Deaf community would be able to participate. Unfortunately, the interpreter was not very skilled, the presenters assumed the audience had a good grasp on the anatomy and physiology of the human body, and very few visuals were used in the presentations. Although pleased to be included in the workshop, the Deaf leaders were unable to follow many of the lectures (personal communication, anonymous, 2004). Also, Deaf people struggle with communicating with medical personnel when they visit hospitals because there is no sign language interpreter (Wilson & Kakiri, 2005).

Many Deaf people also fear the lack of confidentiality if they do have an interpreter (usually a family member or hearing friend who knows some sign language) and fear getting tested for HIV/AIDS or discussing the subject with service professionals. These fears may be well founded as Deaf communities are usually tight-knit and gossip can travel quickly. Meletse experienced such a breach of confidentiality after discussing his HIV+ status with a local Deaf organization social worker.

> A few days later I went there again and the Deaf development worker and Deaf cleaner saw me arriving. They asked me, "Are you HIV positive?" I was extremely shocked and asked, "Who told you that?" They answered, "I just knew that myself". I understood what had happened. The social worker had been gossiping about me. I didn't want to see that social worker anymore. (Meletse & Morgan, this volume, p. S20).

In general, many nations do not recognize the civil rights of their citizens with disabilities so that education, employment, and access to appropriate support and services are beyond their reach. People with disabilities throughout the world have higher rates of illiteracy, fewer employment opportunities, a more likely chance of being placed in an institution or experiencing social isolation and rejection than those who are not disabled (United Nations Disability Statistics, 1993). This lack of recognition of rights leaves people with disabilities to be treated like children throughout their lives and leads some cultures to wrongly believe that people with disabilities are not at risk for HIV/AIDS because they are socially isolated, are sexually inactive, are not prone to drug use, nor at risk of being sexually abused (Groce, 2003).

Risk of infection

Although those involved in HIV/AIDS planning may not see the need to include Deaf people in their programming, research is beginning to indicate that people with disabilities are at an increased risk for every known risk factor of HIV/AIDS. Groce (2003) cites several studies that indicate HIV/AIDS could be a serious problem for people with disabilities (see also UNICEF, 1999). There has been a significant rise in rape of disabled children and adults in cultures where it is believed that HIV+ individuals can rid themselves of the virus by having sex with virgins, and the disabled are thought to be virgins or are vulnerable because they are believed to be unable to act as reliable witnesses on their own behalf when testifying to the police or in a court setting (Chenoweth, 1996; Nosek, Howland & Hughes, 2001; Groce & Trasi, 2004; Wilson & Kakiri, 2005). People with disabilities, especially women, are likely to have more sexual partners than their non-disabled peers since poverty and social taboos against marrying a disabled person mean they are likely to have sexual relationships with various men, rather than only in a stable, monogamous relationship (Rousso, 1995; Groce, 2003).

Further suggestions

Without Deaf people standing up and making their presence and needs known, and without their input to HIV/AIDS organizations on how to reach and offer assistance to the Deaf community, Deaf people may be overlooked and excluded from services and information normally available to others in their region. Some suggestions are:

- Deaf leaders can investigate which governmental and non-profit organizations are working on the issue of HIV/AIDS in their home region and make them aware of the special needs of the Deaf community and insist that Deaf people, as citizens of the local community, be included in all the activities provided to the general public. Most likely it will be the Deaf people's responsibility to educate the organizations on how to make all information accessible, whether it is through quality interpreting, the captioning or interpreting of television programs, or the rewriting or creation of visual materials presented in a format easily understood by those in the Deaf community. Deaf leaders may suggest that hospital and clinic personnel are taught how to communicate with Deaf clients through writing, interpreters, or even by learning some basic signs concerning HIV/AIDS. Some countries train local leaders to be HIV/AIDS educators; they could ask Deaf leaders to participate in order that Deaf people themselves can then educate others in their native sign language.

- Often, Deaf leaders in developing countries are males who may exclude females from leadership positions for various cultural, social, or economic reasons. In many countries, women may be more vulnerable than men in contracting HIV/AIDS. For this reason, it is important to emphasize that women should be included in all programs that the Deaf community participates in and/or creates for themselves. It may be that for some countries, forming Deaf women's groups concerning HIV/AIDS would be more culturally appropriate and would be more effective at conveying the information to other women.

- If an organization, foreign or domestic, approaches the Deaf community to offer assistance in HIV/AIDS training or education, the Deaf community should demand that Deaf leaders (men and women) participate in all aspects of the project budgeting, planning, implementation and evaluation of the program This will ensure transparency, sustainability, eventual independence from the organization offering assistance, and the appropriate provision of services (Wilson, 2005).

- Deaf communities should attempt to network with one another to share materials, information, and knowledge across regions, countries, and continents. As the collection of articles in this journal will demonstrate, there already exist programs that are making an impact on HIV/AIDS education and care in the Deaf community. Perhaps regional conferences sponsored by national Deaf Associations can be held where promising programs, lessons learned, informational workshops, trainings, and collaborative grant writing can be shared and partnerships can be formed.

For Deaf people, the risk of contracting the HIV virus is at least at the same as and probably higher than that of their hearing counterparts. It is their human right to receive information and services concerning HIV/AIDS. Governmental and nongovernmental organizations should be cognizant, but are often unaware, that they are excluding and marginalizing the Deaf community from their programs. Deaf leaders can educate and collaborate with these organizations about the needs of their Deaf communities.

References

Adoyo, P. O. (this volume). A report on the Nyaweri HIV/AIDS Awareness Project of the Deaf in Kenya.

Berenz, N. (this volume). HIV/AIDS in the Brazilian Deaf community: A personal note.

Chenoweth, L. (1993). Invisible Acts: Violence against Women with Disabilities. *Australian Disability Review, 93,* 22–28.

Collins, P., Geller, P., Miller, S., Toro, P. & Susser, E. (2001). Ourselves, our bodies, our realities: an HIV prevention intervention for women with severe mental illness. *Journal of Urban Health: Bulletin of the New York Academy of Medicine, 78,* 162–175.

El Maerrawi, I. (this volume). A program for preventing sexually transmitted diseases for Deaf people in the city of São Vicente, São Paulo, Brazil.

Fedorowicz, S. C. (this volume). Living partial truths: HIV/AIDS in the Japanese deaf world.

Gaskins S. (1999). Special population: STI/HIV/AIDS among the deaf and hard of hearing. *Journal of the Association of Nurses in AIDS Care, 35,* 75–78.

Ghaji, A. (2002). Disabled women: An excluded agenda of India feminism. *Hypatia, 17,* 49–66.

Goldstein, M. F., Eckhardt, E., Joyner, P., & Berry, R. (this volume). An HIV knowledge and attitude survey of Deaf U.S. adults.

Groce, N. (2003). HIV/AIDS and people with disability. *The Lancet, 361,* 1401–1402.

Groce, N., & Trasi, R. (2004). Rape of individuals with disability: AIDS and the folk belief of virgin cleansing. *The Lancet, 363,* 1663–1664.

Henderson, K. (this volume). Short report of Liverpool VCT and Care (LVCT) work in progress.

Heyerick, I. (this volume). HIV/AIDS and Deafness in Flanders.

Mäkipää, A. (1993). WFD delegation at WHO: Medical profession needs a new approach to deafness. *World Federation of the Deaf News, 2,* 15–17.

Maclons, K. (this volume). Opening the door of life skills, HIV and AIDS education for the South African Deaf learner.

Malmquist, C. P. (1985). *Handbook of adolescence.* New York: Aronson.

Meletse, J., & Morgan, R. (this volume). "I have two!": Personal reflections of a Deaf HIV positive gay man in South Africa.

Monaghan, L. (this volume). Maryland 2003 HIV infection statistics for hearing and Deaf populations: Analysis and policy suggestions.

Nosek, M. A., Howland, C. A., & Hughes, R. B. (2001). The investigation of abuse and women with disabilities: Going beyond assumptions. *Violence Against Women, 7,* 477– 499.

Perlman, T. S., & Leon, S. C. (this volume). Preventing AIDS in the Midwest: The design and efficacy of culturally sensitive HIV/AIDS prevention education materials for Deaf communities.

Peters, S. (2003, May). *Inclusive education: Achieving education for all by including those with disabilities and special education needs.* Report prepared for the World Bank Disability Group.

Poor, B. (this volume). Brad.

Roberts, G. S. (this volume). Sexuality and HIV/AIDS education among Deaf and hard of hearing students.

Robertson, P., Bhate S., & Bhate, M. (1991). AIDS: education and adults with a mental handicap. *Journal of Mental Deficiency, 35,* 475–480.

Rousso, H. (1995). *Education for all: A gender and disability perspective.* Unpublished report for the World Bank. Retrieved July 16, 2005, from http://64.233.161.104/search?q=cache:qlVhLisJmuYJ:siteresources. worldbank.org/DISABILITY/Resources/Education/Education_for_All _A_Gender_and_Disability_Perspective.doc+Education+for+All:+A +Gender+and+Disability+Perspective&hl=en

Schmaling, C., & Loum, D. (this volume). The first HIV/AIDS education project for deaf people in The Gambia.

Scofield, J., & Fineberg, R. (2002). *Educating children with disabilities in developing nations: A roundtable dialogue, November 12, 2002*. Washington, D.C.: Creative Associates International.

Sleek, S. (1998). STI/HIV/AIDS education efforts have missed deaf community. *American Psychological Association Monitor Online*. Retrieved July 16, 2005, from http://www.apa.org/monitor/oct98/hiv.html.

UNAIDS. (2002). *Report on the global HIV/AIDS epidemic 2002*. New York: Joint UN Programme on HIV/AIDS.

UNICEF. (1999). *Global survey of adolescents with disability: An overview of young people living with disabilities: their needs and their rights*. New York: UNICEF Inter-Divisional Working Group on Young People, Programme Division.

United Nations. (2005). *An exceptional response to AIDS*. Retrieved July 15, 2005, from http://www.unaids.org/NetTools/Misc/DocInfo.aspx? LANG=en&href=http://gva-doc owl/WEBcontent/Documents/pub/Publications/ IRC pub05/JC1117-ExceptionalResponse_en.pdf

United Nations Disability Division. (1993). *Human functioning and disability Demographic yearbook special issue: Population ageing and the situation of elderly persons, 1993*. Retrieved July 16, 2005, from http://unstats.un.org/unsd/demographic/sconcerns/disability/dybCh6Notes.pdf

United Nations Population Fund. (2005). *AIDS Clock*. Retrieved August 18, 2005, from http://www.unfpa.org/aids_clock/main.htm

Van Biema, D. (1994, April 4). AIDS and the Deaf. *Time Magazine, 143 (14)*, 76-77.

Wilson, A. (2005). Studying the effectiveness of international development assistance, from American organizations to Deaf communities in Jamaica. *American Annals of the Deaf, 150*, 292–304.

Wilson, A., and Kakiri, N. (2005). *Final report: A survey of the development assistance desired by deaf Kenyans. Report to Kenyan Ministry of Education*. Washington, D.C.: Gallaudet University.

World Health Organization. (1999). *Director-General urges comprehensive agenda on disability.* World Health Organization Press Release, December 3, 1999. Retrieved July 16, 2005, from http://www.who. int/inf-pr-1999/en/pr99-68.html

World Bank. (2004). *HIV/AIDS and disability: Capturing hidden voices.* Retrieved July 16, 2005, from http://globalsurvey.med.yale.edu/ Capturing%20hidden%20voices-1.pdf

Contact information
Amy T. Wilson, Ph.D.
Program Director, Master's of Arts Degree in International Development
Department of Educational Foundations and Research
Gallaudet University
406 Fowler Hall
800 Florida Avenue, NE
Washington, D.C. 20009
Tel/TTY: +1 202 651 5201
Fax: +1 202 651 5710
email: amy.wilson@gallaudet.ed
Leila Monaghan, Ph.D.
Course Director, Interpersonal Communication
Department of Communication and Culture
Indiana University
1760 E. 10th Street
Bloomington, IN 47405-9700
Tel: +1 812 855 4607
Fax: +1 812 855 6014
email: monaghan@indiana.edu

"I have two!": Personal reflections of a Deaf HIV positive gay man in South Africa

John Meletse with Ruth Morgan

Deaf Worlds
2006 | vol 22 (1)
Forest Books ©
ISSN 1362–3125

Key words
Deafness, HIV / AIDS, life story, gay, South Africa, disclosure

Biographies
John Meletse is the Deaf Gay Oral History Project and Outreach officer at the Gay and Lesbian Archives of South Africa (GALA). He is also involved in GALA's HIV Oral History and Outreach Project.

Ruth Morgan is the Director of GALA. She has a Ph.D. in linguistic anthropology from the American University, Washington D.C., and an M.A. in linguistics from Gallaudet University, Washington D.C.

Introduction
I am a twenty-nine year old Deaf black South African gay man and I am also HIV positive. I am writing this article with my hearing colleague Ruth Morgan who is assisting with the translation from South African Sign Language. We both work for the Gay and Lesbian Archives of South Africa (GALA). I am responsible for the Deaf Gay Oral History Project and Diversity Training Outreach Programme. Ruth is the director of GALA.

In this paper I focus on my personal reflections on different aspects of my life story as a Deaf gay black man who is HIV positive. In this process I am also drawing on my videotaped and transcribed life story interview. Ruth interviewed me recently as we needed to update my life story which we have been recording for GALA over the past four years. We have decided to structure this paper around excerpts from my life story which highlight an important topic in my journey of coming to terms with being HIV positive. The excerpts – in italics – are then followed by my reflections on these events.

The first time I thought I was positive

....I think that was in 2002 ....yes! And then there was a letter that I received....at home. My grandmother gave me the letter and wanted to know who it was from and then this letter said I have Aids. And I was shocked. I said 'what, I have Aids!?'. I felt very vulnerable and then the following day I went to work, it was extremely stressful me, very stressful. I asked the interpreter I was working with....I told her about the story and it was shocking, I couldn't work. The only thing I could do was to think about this. I passed out and I was taken to the clinic....Someone else phoned a doctor and they came to pick me up and I was taken to Wits University Health Campus....Health Center. And the doctor did some tests and said you are negative, the HIV test was negative. I was very relieved about that.

I still don't know who sent me the letter informing me that I had AIDS. Perhaps someone saw that I was very thin and assumed that I had AIDS and maliciously sent me that letter. I had to stay in the hospital because of the stress that the letter caused me. It made me ill! The doctors tested me again at the hospital and thankfully I was negative. I was hugely relieved and very happy about that. I remember my grandmother telling me to look after myself after I had been in the hospital. I was determined to take care of my health and remain negative. I would be careful to have safe sex from now on.

Date rape

Then I found another hearing boyfriend in Soweto. We were together for a while and so we slept together, he wanted sex and I said that we have to use a condom, he said that was fine with him. He gave me wine to drink mixed with coca cola and that made me very drunk. I couldn't remember anything. The following morning I was naked and I said 'What's happening?' and he said 'Well I had sex with you', I said 'Really'. And then it was very stressful for me thinking about it but I just went to work everyday.

Alcohol and drugs are a huge problem in the gay community as many people find themselves having had unprotected sex without knowing it. My next boyfriend slept with me without a condom, without my consent. I would never have agreed to this. I had no idea that he had started to mix my coke with wine. I couldn't remember anything the next morning. I didn't know why I was naked and had no idea that we had had sex until he told me. I asked him if he had used a condom as we had discussed. He said he hadn't used anything. I left and was really stressed as I was worrying about my HIV status. I couldn't stop thinking about that. He tried to make me forget about that by sweet-talking me but I couldn't stop thinking that I was infected for about two weeks. I never went for a test. I never told anyone about what had happened. I did nothing until November 2003.

HIV diagnosis

And then I started feeling weak again…. that's right and I went to the hospital in Soweto, to a clinic in Soweto and I said I would like to have a (HIV) test done. And there was no counselor, they just said you want the test done, so they took blood from my finger and they said you can wait for 15 minutes. And I was given the test results there and then it was thrown into my face and it was positive. I said 'What! Me! Positive!'. I couldn't believe it nor could I understand it. They said 'Yes you are', but there was no counseling, no counseling at all. This made me very angry, I sent a text message to Ruth and I said 'I am positive'. So I waited and I stayed home for three days. As I went into the house I saw my grandmother and I started to cry. My granny just said 'Why are you crying?'. I said 'I am positive' and my granny said 'Don't worry it will be fine, don't worry it doesn't matter there are many people (who are positive) in the world.'

I still remember how I went to the local clinic near my home as I wasn't feeling well. I will never forget what happened there as the nurses and doctor treated me without respect due to the fact that I am a Deaf person. I went there without a sign language interpreter. I want to include all the details of what happened that day as I remember them vividly. I had been feeling weak. I arrived at the clinic and I said to the nursing sister "Hi, I'm Deaf". I could lip read that the sister said "Shame" (a South African expression of sympathy) as she felt sorry for me because I was Deaf. I was confused as to why she was pitying me as there was a sign language poster on the wall of the clinic showing South African Sign Language vocabulary for medical terms. I sat down with her and we had difficulty communicating. She asked another nurse to come and help with the communication – we tried writing back and forth. She asked if I understood English and I said I did. The other nurse was also feeling sorry for me and saying "Shame" and I got frustrated and fed up as they weren't respecting me. I went in to see the doctor. He was a black doctor so I was happy to see that at first. The sister explained that I was Deaf. The doctor said that was ok. I told the doctor that I needed an HIV test. They did not give me any counseling which is required in South Africa. The doctor did the test and told me to wait for 15 minutes outside until he could give me the results. I was very anxious. The doctor called me back and wrote on a piece of paper in large letters "YOU ARE HIV POSITIVE". He put it in my face. I felt shocked and sick – I mouthed "Is this true?" He nodded "yes". He said "Goodbye you can go now". I was so shocked, I sent Ruth a text message, saying "I am HIV positive". I walked home crying. My grandmother could see me coming with tears streaming down my face. She asked me what had happened. I told her that I was positive. She told me not to worry and to stop crying. I explained to her what had happened at the clinic.

I could not believe the way I was treated at the clinic as Voluntary Counseling and Testing requires that people are counseled both before and after being tested for HIV. This was not done in my case because I was Deaf. Other people were also being discriminated against in this way such as youth who were also not counseled. At that clinic they only seemed to be counseling the hearing adults. It is important for Deaf people to be treated with respect and dignity at clinics. This is our constitutional right in South Africa. I was too shocked at the news of my status to report the doctor to the medical authorities.

Dealing with the shock

My grandmother was telling my mom that her son, who is me, was HIV positive and then my mother didn't want to believe that. So we left it and my mom just said she wouldn't believe this and I stayed at home for three days and that's all I could think about....My granny just said 'Don't think about it try and sleep, don't worry' but it wasn't possible for me. I just thought about myself being HIV positive.

It is very important to have support when you are given such a diagnosis. The day I found out that I was positive my grandmother was very supportive of me. However my mother just didn't believe that I was positive as she couldn't accept the situation. She told me that the clinic didn't know anything and they probably didn't do the test correctly and that they were probably lying about this. But I believed the test result. My grandmother told me to ignore my mother as she also believed the test result. My grandmother went to look for a HIV publication that she gave me to read so that I could get more information about HIV. She asked me if I understood everything. I said that the problem was that I was feeling weak and couldn't take it all in, especially the complicated vocabulary. My grandmother brought me water to drink and told me not to worry. My mother kept on wanting to know if I was ok and told me not to believe the doctor.

In search of counseling and information

And then I received a text message from Ruth, she told me about Jacob (a gay HIV counselor), and said that I should go to the clinic and seen him. I did and I found Jacob and I didn't know this person but anyway I sat down with him and we started writing back and forth, I couldn't understand the English (as he was using big words). He said he has been positive for five years and I thought he said that I would die in five years. I said 'How can that be?'. So I left him.

For three days I rested and I came to work. I met with Ruth and she gave me some advice which was wonderful. And she said you must go to Lazarus (my Deaf mentor) and I then went to Lazarus and said 'I am HIV positive'.

Lazarus even tried to refer me to clinics and he said there are many Deaf people who are HIV positive. And I decided to go to Baragwanath hospital (the biggest hospital in South African located in Soweto) and there was a person, an Indian interpreter, who did not sign very well. An interview was done....some counseling and so I had another test done and it came back, more counseling was done, and the doctor explained the result and said 'Yes you are positive, you have to be careful, you need to wear condoms'. This made me feel a little more relieved as I started to understand everything.

And then I went to work and Robin (my interpreter) was there....I sat down with her and I couldn't understand why she looked at me in that way. She looked at me and said, 'Why aren't you happy anymore?' because I obviously was sad. She said 'Do you

want some crisps?' and she nagged me, she came back and she wanted to know why I
was angry. I said 'I'm just not happy' and I was open and honest with her then I said
'I am HIV positive' and she just said to me 'Don't worry I'll be your friend I'll support
you' and I accepted that for what it is worth.

And then Ruth also gave me counseling and a lot of advice. And I went to Carol for
some more advice and I was told by Carol that I needed to take some vitamins and get
medication. I didn't know anything about these things.

When I went there (to the clinic) the doctor gave me some pills. At first I went with
Amanda, she was my interpreter. She interpreted and she just said to me: 'I am so sorry
my friend that you are HIV positive but I still love you are my friend, don't worry I'll
still have a good relationship with you.' And I was so relieved because I thought
perhaps she would reject me, and she said 'You've been my friend for four years and
you will still be my friend', so we laughed about it and she gave me a hug. She then
left and thought a lot about it. I took some pills and keep taking these pills.

It took a long time for me to be able to access the information and support
I needed as a Deaf gay person. It was very frustrating due to the lack of sign
language interpreters and the problems I had communicating with people.
I am now going to explain my experiences in more details than I did in my
life story interview quoted above. I feel the need to do so as there were
frustrations at every corner. The worst thing was that I had a lot of problems
at the local Deaf organization which is where I thought I could get a lot of
support.

Ruth had initially suggested I go to Jacob as he was a hearing gay
counselor at the clinic who had been living positively for five years. He
worked at the clinic where I had been diagnosed and she had organized for
me to see him that very same day that I was diagnosed. I went back to the
clinic and Jacob tried to communicate with me by writing. I couldn't
understand what he wrote as he used very difficult and complicated
vocabulary and I was still in shock. I misunderstood him and also thought
that he had told me that I would die in five years. That made me feel worse
and I was very nervous about that. Ruth later explained that Jacob was
trying to tell me that he was fine and healthy after being positive for five
years. Jacob then phoned Ruth and said he needed a SASL interpreter to
communicate with me properly. He phoned a local Deaf organization and

asked for an interpreter. As there was no interpreter there they offered their social worker who did not have strong sign language skills. Jacob didn't know that it could be possible for a Deaf organization to have a social worker who couldn't sign properly so he set up an appointment. When Ruth heard that Jacob had arranged to go with me to the Deaf organization, she told Jacob that it wasn't a good idea and told him to cancel the appointment. She said she would arrange for a qualified interpreter to interpret a counseling session for me. I then had a counseling session with the psychologist who was facilitating the gay support group for HIV infected and affected people that I was already attending.

I then also went myself to the Deaf organization and told a staff member that I was positive. I thought I could get some help directly from him as he is also Deaf. However he referred me to the hearing social worker that worked there. The social worker couldn't sign very well. I told her that I was positive and she wasn't very helpful. A few days later I went there again and the Deaf development worker and Deaf cleaner saw me arriving. They asked me "Are you HIV positive?" I was extremely shocked and asked "Who told you that?" They answered "I just knew that myself". I understood what had happened. The social worker had been gossiping about me. I didn't want to see that social worker anymore.

Ruth explained to me more about HIV and suggested I go to talk to my Deaf mentor Lazarus who had taught me at high school and had known me for a long time. He explained that I needed to go for another test and to get proper counseling. It could happen that the tests would have different results. If I was positive for two consecutive tests then it would be true. He advised me to go to the big hospital – Baragwanath – in Soweto where there is a special HIV wellness clinic which Ruth had also referred me to. He said I needed to also eat well to stay healthy and told me not to worry. He also said that I shouldn't worry as there are Deaf positive people in all the provinces. He reassured me that I was not the only one. He let me know that he would still support me and that many other people such as Ruth would also support me. After this discussion I decided that I would go to Baragwanath Hospital for another test.

I finally went to the clinic next to Baragwanath Hospital, the Perinatal HIV Research Unit (PHRU) clinic where I received proper counseling with a skilled interpreter who volunteered to interpret for me. They arranged for counseling and another test. I had counseling again after I got the test result. A doctor also saw me the following week. That time I had no interpreter with me and the Indian woman who knew a little sign language tried to assist me. They gave me a piece of paper that I didn't understand. I brought it to Ruth and she explained it all to me. They wanted to know if I would take part in a research study. I agreed. I needed to go there every month. They also did a CD4 test and I didn't understand what CD4 meant. They also mentioned something about a viral load which I didn't understand. I asked Ruth who explained it all to me. She also explained to me that there were people like Edwin Cameron and Zackie Achmat who had been HIV positive for many years and they were still healthy. Ruth arranged to interpret for me while I got more counseling from an HIV peer counselor at the university. Everything was slowly becoming clear although I frequently felt confused and I didn't want to read any more written information. It was explained to me what the supplements were that the doctor at the clinic had prescribed. I didn't need anti-retrovirals yet.

The Deaf community's response

I did not include the following incidents in my life story interview. I have thought about this a lot and want to explain the difficulties I experienced as a result of ignorance in the Deaf community about HIV and AIDS. The malicious gossip really hurt me a lot and this turned out to be more traumatic than the fact that I was positive.

A few weeks later I received a text message from someone saying that I had AIDS. There was no person's name after the message. I didn't say anything about that to anyone. Later I started getting text messages from many Deaf people saying that they heard I had AIDS. Some Deaf people thought I had already died. I was extremely upset and cried a lot. I didn't know who was spreading the rumours. Even my boyfriend in Durban heard about this and accused me of not saying anything to him about my HIV status. This caused us to separate. The Deaf spreading rumours were responsible for this. I still loved him. I went to visit him and later he visited me. We sat down and discussed everything. We discovered we were both HIV positive and hadn't told each other. Everything was now clear. He went back to Durban. Eventually the relationship fizzled out.

On 1 December 2003 I went to the national Deaf organization's training workshop for HIV counseling and training. People from all the provinces attended. I was the only one who never received a certificate. I felt that the reason for this was the hearing social worker who ran the workshop didn't want Deaf people to become counselors in Johannesburg. I left feeling very angry and fed up as the other provinces all had Deaf counselors except for Johannesburg.

Disclosure to extended family as both gay and HIV positive

….I sent a text message to (my colleagues) Ruth and Busi to remind them to watch my short film (I have two!) and I watched it and I was very thrilled to see my acting on TV. And my family was called, everybody was called together I was shocked and they said we understand that you are gay but why didn't you inform the aunt and I said 'I must tell others about it and this is my life'. They said 'Why have you kept quiet for such a long time? We knew that you were gay but everybody could see the way you walk and your body'….my aunt said everybody could see. Everybody always wanted to know …and many people were just so happy for me, so we had a braai (barbecue) and some drinks and I was very relieved.

….They waited for me to say something as they kind of knew I was gay. My sister was interpreting she doesn't sign very well….so I could understand what she says. And then I also told my grandmother who informed the rest of the family that I was HIV positive, yet they didn't quite believe it, that I was HIV positive because they never saw me with a girlfriend. Yes they support me, they are happy for me, they understand that I am gay, my sisters all of them understand that.

My grandmother and myself decided that I needed to inform my extended family that I was both gay and HIV positive before they saw my short film about my life as a black Deaf gay man on national television. In October 2004 I attended the Building Bridges conference on Deaf education where I did a poster presentation on Deaf gay issues in schools and screened my short film "I have two!". I was interviewed by Deaf TV (DTV) and the interview and excerpts from my film were screened on national television. At that gathering, my family accepted that I was gay and didn't have a problem as they already knew that I was effeminate after watching me grow up. However they were really shocked to hear that I was HIV positive. I knew that I had a straight cousin who was HIV positive but he had not disclosed this to anyone. They didn't understand how I had become positive as they hadn't seen me with a girlfriend. In actual fact, my extended family didn't understand how a gay person could get HIV – they were ignorant about HIV in the gay community as they had only observed it in heterosexual relationships. I had never shown them my boyfriends so they didn't know I had been having relationships. They didn't really understand much about being gay and same sex relationships. Later that night I chatted to my grandmother who felt relieved that the family now knew that I was HIV positive and gay. My father wasn't there at the meeting but he knew about my status and has always been very supportive.

Outing by Deaf development worker at World AIDS Day 2004

My problems with the Deaf community continued. I was invited by a local Deaf organization to give a talk at their World AIDS Day programme last year (2004). I had not publicly disclosed my status at that point. I accepted to give a talk on HIV. While I was giving a talk on the need for a support group, the Deaf development worker walked past and said to everyone, "There's John who's HIV positive". Everyone there was shocked and started talking about this to each other. I was not at all happy – I finished my talk and carried on as normal but I was extremely shocked that she had outed me in public. My colleagues and peers came up to me and said "How can you be HIV positive, you look healthy and fine". I went back to my office and felt awful. That night I got another abusive text message that said AIDS without any sender's name. I felt weak. The next morning I went to see Lazarus again and his colleague. They were also very upset on my behalf at the unethical behaviour of the Deaf development worker – they said "That's seriously bad!". Lazarus wanted to write a letter of complaint to the director of the Deaf organization. I told him not to as I didn't think it would help. I carried on being upset about this.

Being a role model in the GALA outreach diversity training progamme

With the assistance of Karl Reddy, I have recently developed a diversity training pilot programme for local Deaf schools around Johannesburg. Our training deals with HIV issues, sexuality issues and cross cultural issues.

There is a specific focus on HIV. At these workshops I openly disclose to the learners that I am both gay and HIV positive. This helps the learners become sensitive to me. It is important for learners to know that I am both Deaf and HIV positive as Deaf learners do not have any HIV positive role models. In the hearing world learners have many HIV positive role models such as Zackie Achmat and Edwin Cameron who have come out as HIV positive publicly on television and in the HIV activist world. However in the Deaf world HIV is still highly stigmatized and there are no Deaf people that I know of besides myself who are publicly out as HIV positive. That is why I decided this year after a long process of 15 months of coming to terms with being HIV positive myself to come out and disclose my status to the Deaf world.

Although we are only doing a pilot programme in the schools, the response so far has been excellent. One of the schools for Deaf learners informed me that they are aware of two HIV positive young Deaf learners there and asked me to continue visiting the school on a regular basis. They also explained that the Deaf teaching assistants were not coping with the situation and were having difficulty relating to these children which was making the situation worse. They asked me to come and help the Deaf assistants understand HIV issues in more depth. Another school had one HIV positive learner and they too asked me to continue giving their learners input on HIV. Although some of the schools have excellent videotaped and written material developed for Deaf learners that includes a focus on HIV developed by SLED (Sign Language Education and Development), the learners want a real Deaf person such as myself to give them the information they need. Deaf schools have hearing teachers without South African Sign Language interpreters. In many cases the Deaf learners have trouble understanding these teachers. The learners at the schools that we have visited are therefore not well informed about HIV. They don't have posters about safe sex or voluntary counseling and testing. They don't understand why it is important to have safe sex, how the virus is transmitted or why there is a need to be tested. They also don't understand the concepts of CD4 counts, viral load and sexually transmitted infections (STIs). In my workshops I explain these things to them.

Although I can disclose my status to the children, it is impossible for them to disclose if they are HIV positive to their teachers or peers. There is still so much ignorance about HIV in Deaf schools. Both teachers and learners stigmatise children that are positive. There is a lot of work for me to do in schools to help them deal with the situation.

Living positively: Being out and proud

It was only very recently in May 2005 that I was ready to come out to everyone as HIV positive! I made this decision after being outed at the end of last year. After getting over being very upset by the fact that the Deaf community now knew about my status, I realized that there are no role models of healthy Deaf HIV positive people. I discussed this with Deaf mentor Lazarus and my hearing colleagues at GALA who also encouraged me to be strong and open about who I am. By being open, all the gossip would have to stop. I have put on weight since I have been eating healthily and maintained my health by regular visits to the HIV wellness clinic where I get supplements and medication when I need it. I still don't need anti-retrovirals. I have also attended workshops about HIV and want to educate as many Deaf people as possible about the virus.

Reflections on the general situation in South Africa and my role in the future

In South Africa, there is a very high incidence of HIV positive people in the general population. There are high levels of stigma still attached to being HIV positive. People are dying without treatment. They don't want to know their status and refuse to be tested when they are still healthy. People only start doing something when they are extremely thin and weak. They wait until they get sick and then decide to go to the HIV clinic. At that point they have to wait months for an appointment at the HIV clinic as they are not a known patient and have no file at the clinic. They need to be put on a waiting list and sometimes they die before they get an appointment. If they are admitted to hospital often they are too sick to respond to ARV treatment and its too late for them to get help.

Deaf people cannot access the free help HIV AIDS hotline and cannot get counseling and information that is available to hearing people. Here are some of my ideas to increase accessibility to services for Deaf people. There needs to be a free text message service set up for Deaf people to access HIV information and counseling. Existing HIV clinics and programmes throughout South Africa need to train and employ Deaf HIV counselors so that Deaf people can access their services in urban and rural areas. I am committed to working with GALA to raise awareness about HIV in the Deaf community and to be a role model for all Deaf people who are HIV positive. My work with Deaf learners who are still at school is very important and I hope to extend this project into all provinces. I would like to train other Deaf people to be HIV peer educators and counselors. It is very important that Deaf people do this to ensure that the information is understood by the Deaf community.

Contact information

John Meletse and Ruth Morgan
Gay and Lesbian Archives of South Africa
PO Box 31719
Braamfontein
2017
South Africa
Tel: +27117174239
Fax: +27117171783
email: meletse_j@yahoo.com and morganr@gala.wits.ac.za

Opening the door of life skills, HIV and AIDS education for the South African Deaf learner

Kirsty Maclons on behalf of the SLED team

Deaf Worlds
2006 | vol 22 (1)
Forest Books ©
ISSN 1362–3125

Key words

South Africa, HIV/AIDS, South African Sign Language, Deaf youth, Deaf schools, educational videos

Abstract

As a Deaf organisation, SLED (Sign Language Education and Development) is delighted to have created, filmed, produced and edited *Life Skills, HIV and AIDS Education for the Deaf Learner* videos as well as written materials for the National Department of Health. This is not just another adaptation of existing materials to 'suit' the needs of the Deaf but an original and innovative project specifically aimed at the Deaf learner at school. All the materials are obviously African and reflect both urban and rural real life situations in Sub Saharan Africa. The Deaf community and teachers of the Deaf have applauded these materials for their creative content, unique use of SASL and a 'hands-on' understanding of the obstacles regarding written language development that are faced by Deaf learners. SLED has been hosting training workshops, aimed at empowering teachers, Deaf teaching assistants and caregivers of Deaf learners with the necessary skills to be able to use these materials effectively. These workshops have encouraged teachers to re-look at the way we teach Deaf learners, and many regard the workshops as the turning point for themselves and their schools. SLED has run these workshops at most of the schools for the Deaf in South Africa. The Minster of Health, Dr M. Tshabalala-Msimang, and the Minister of Education, Prof K. Asmal, officially launched this project in March 2004 at a high profile event in Eldorado Park, south of Johannesburg.

Biographies (Members of the SLED team)

Growing up as a Deaf child in a Deaf family, **Atiyah Asmal**, has been surrounded by South African Sign Language (SASL) since she was born. She teaches SASL to Deaf children, teachers, university students and parents. Since 1996 she has been working as a presenter for television programmes for Deaf children. Atiyah has been the focus of the training workshops that have been held for the *Life Skills, HIV and AIDS Education for the Deaf Learner* project. Her demonstration lessons have shown her not only to have a unique understanding of the Deaf community but also to be an exceptional and empathetic teacher. She is currently studying towards a degree in linguistics.

Nazereen Bhana's public career started in 1994 when she became one of the first Deaf presenters on South African television. Prior to this she taught SASL and Life Skills in a school for the Deaf. She would also accompany social workers when they visited the parents of a Deaf child, helping them to understand the unique language and needs of the child. This work was nationally recognised when she won the Avanti Award for Best Presenter in 1997. She is the vice chairperson of the Gauteng Deaf Provincial Committee and the creative force for the SASL courses for students from the Faculty of Education and Nursing at the University of Johannesburg.

While working as a teacher of the Deaf, **Cara Loening** founded the SA Theatre of the Deaf in Cape Town. In 1996 she began working on Deaf programmes for the South African Broadcasting Corporation as a director, researcher and interpreter, helping the project produce 25 SASL videos that showcased the talents of South Africa's Deaf storytellers and poets. Cara has been responsible for co-ordinating the *Life Skills, HIV and AIDS Education for the Deaf Learner* project since its inception.

Kirsty Maclons is an enthusiastic campaigner for the empowerment of the Deaf community and its language, SASL. She is a qualified teacher of the Deaf who has over 18 years of experience in various fields of Deaf education from school to university level. Kirsty has been responsible for the expert facilitation of the training workshops held at schools for the Deaf across the country for the *Life Skills, HIV and AIDS Education for the Deaf Learner* project.

Modiegi Moime has worked as a field reporter and researcher for Deaf television programmes since 1997. She is a highly respected Deaf poet who has received national and international recognition for her work from both the Deaf and hearing communities. She has been involved in training the hearing and Deaf teachers and Deaf learners as part of the *Life Skills, HIV and AIDS Education for the Deaf Learner* workshops that we are currently running for the national Department of Health.

Abram Moyaha is a gifted Deaf artist who can capture the essence of the life and experience of the South African Deaf community with a stroke of his pen as well as being a skilled actor. In 2000 he represented South Africa at the International Drama Festival for the Deaf in Madrid, Spain, with a production entitled 'Have you heard?' He shows a unique empathy for the Deaf learner during the workshops run by SLED throughout South Africa.

Introduction
South African Sign Language (SASL) is the most basic human right of the Deaf Community and has become widely recognised and protected in various legislative and governmental policies – and even acknowledged as a language of education equal in status to the eleven official languages in the country. And yet, the dearth of material and trained teachers in SASL creates a situation where this recognition is almost meaningless unless proper training can take place and suitable material be developed.

It was through the reality of this situation that SLED (Sign Language Education and Development) was born. The main purpose of this non-profit Deaf organisation is the upliftment of the Deaf child through the creation and promotion of South African Sign Language programmes, services and materials. Our mission is to provide the Deaf child and the Deaf community of South Africa with an equal and democratic right to learning and access to information through the promotion of South African Sign Language.

SLED is a predominantly Deaf organisation made up of professional people with many years of expertise in Deaf education from Grade 0 to Adult Education; television presentation, production, directing and editing; SASL poetry and storytelling; teacher training and SASL interpreting.

HIV and AIDS – The reality in South Africa

Recognising the alarming number of South Africans living with HIV and dying of AIDS, the South African government and various NGOs have embarked on various educational campaigns to educate the youth especially about HIV and AIDS. Unfortunately all of these materials are inaccessible to Deaf youth either because they are not in South African Sign Language or they are in a written language that they cannot access because of high levels of illiteracy among Deaf learners and school leavers.

There is much confusion among the South African Deaf community about many aspects of HIV and AIDS. Many Deaf adults who are told they are HIV positive take this to mean that they do not have the HIVirus, misunderstanding the word positive to mean that they are fine or 'positive'. The advertisements that are prevalent in the urban centres have images and slogans that are often misunderstood by Deaf people.

Life skills, HIV and AIDS education for the Deaf learner

In May 2002, in response to a proposed tender from the National Department of Health the SLED team submitted a proposal as to how we would meet the life skills and HIV/AIDS needs of the Deaf learner through the development of SASL videos, educator manuals and learners activity books. The project was aimed at South African Deaf learners from Pre-School to Grade 9, essentially the first ten years of school.

Later we suggested the use of laminated posters for the teachers and this was added to the project. We also suggested that this project be supported by workshops run at the schools for the Deaf. The various provincial Departments of Education have sponsored these workshops.

Dr Kenau Swart, from the National Department of Health, guided the project with the assistance of a steering committee on which DeafSA (the national Deaf organisation of South Africa), teachers of the Deaf, other NGOs involved in disability and the National Department of Education were represented.

June 2002 – The project commences

We were surprised that we had been awarded such an immense project as we had only been in operation for a few months. However, we were excited to start on the project, as we knew it would be highly beneficial for the Deaf learners of South Africa. After several meetings between the SLED team and the steering committee for the *Life Skills, HIV and AIDS Education for the Deaf Learner* project we commenced on researching what were the major problems facing the Deaf community in terms of HIV and AIDS, sex, abuse and other issues. From this we developed the core ideas for scripts, educator manuals and learners activity books for each phase.

Developing the videos

In June 2002, we started working on the script for the Foundation Phase (Grades 1–3). The team would discuss the script in detail and then revisions would be made. The steering committee approved the script and we set about auditioning the Deaf learners and adults that would be acting in the Foundation Phase video. The script was created as a series of ideas rather than a formal script. This was deliberately done to prevent the Deaf learner/actors from using Signed English rather than South African Sign Language.

We auditioned Deaf learners from numerous schools for the Deaf in Gauteng. We would explain to the Learner Representative Council (a body made up of student representatives from the various grades) at the different schools what the film was about and the characters that would be needed and then ask them to choose a selection of Deaf learners for us to audition.

Developing the manuals

In September 2002, research started on the educator manuals and the learners activity books. The materials had to conform to the aims of the HIV and AIDS Youth Programme of the national Department of Health and the Life Orientation learning area of the national Department of Education.[1]

We also worked with organisations such as Love Life (a governmental programme aimed at educating the youth about HIV and AIDS) and various other AIDS organisations. Then we developed a simple structure for each unit in the educator manual that outlined the learning outcomes for that unit as well as what preparation was needed and what home based activity the learners should do.

Atiyah and Kirsty would primarily work on the written materials in rough format. These would then be presented to the SLED team and the Deaf artists and Deaf graphic artist who would brainstorm the way forward. Atiyah and Kirsty would make the necessary revisions which would then go to the Steering Committee for final approval and other adjustments. After the pilot study several changes were also made to the materials.

We chose four Deaf learners from various schools for the Deaf in the Gauteng area and a Deaf teacher from St Vincent School for the Deaf in Johannesburg. We decided to film at Sizwile School for the Deaf in Dobsonville, a township outside Johannesburg. We worked with the actors to explain the script in SASL asking them what they would do and how they would feel if they found themselves in a similar situation to the character that they were portraying. We wanted them to give us accurate age-appropriate signs used in a natural SASL structure. We filmed for four days and it was great to see how the learners improved their knowledge of HIV and other Life Skills issues and became more confident. The SLED team learned a lot as well and made careful notes so that the next shoot would reflect our newly acquired knowledge.

Filming continues

In late November 2002, we started filming for the Pre-School and Grade R (the reception year) video. The main focus of this video was the vital communication that must occur between a caregiver and her Deaf child. We chose Aviwe Jemane, a Deaf child who was only four years old, whose SASL skills are excellent because she has Deaf parents. Aviwe played the character called Nomsa. We also used an elderly hearing gentleman to play her grandfather and a Deaf woman, Rebecca Magongwa, to act as her mother. We filmed for four days in Tembisa, a township outside Johannesburg. It was a long and difficult shoot but we are delighted with the end product. Aviwe was a natural actress and shows clearly how a Deaf child can keep pace with her hearing counterparts if exposed to SASL from birth.

In February 2003, we auditioned again for the Intermediate Phase video. The Intermediate Phase is Grade 4–6. The SLED team went to the Dominican School for the Deaf in Hammanskraal and Transoranje School for the Deaf in Pretoria to do auditions and decided on four main characters and several background characters. It was great to watch how the four Deaf learners got to know each other so quickly despite never having met before. We filmed over four days and are very happy with the final video. Each story is approximately 25 minutes long and so the total duration of the Intermediate Phase videos is +/- 1 hour 40 minutes.

When it was time to pay these learners for their services, one of our team travelled through to Hammanskraal and took the learners to the local shopping centre so that they could learn the basic life skills of how to look after their own finances and how to pay for goods.

Developing the final script for the Senior Phase – which took place in February 2003 – was perhaps the most difficult as it concentrated on difficult issues such as living with AIDS, peer pressure, date rape and drug abuse. In March 2003, we started filming for the Senior Phase. Again we used four central characters from different schools for the Deaf in Gauteng. We filmed all over Johannesburg in real locations such as a police station, a family planning clinic, and a shopping mall and even in our own offices. What was interesting during this shoot was how much the Deaf actors learnt about the different topics and how often the problems that we were filming were problems that they had encountered in their lives before. All of the videos are an excellent example of SLED's work and we strongly support videos using SASL as providing equitable access for the Deaf community.

Now was the time for the pre-test of the materials. We held a day's workshop at Sizwile School for the Deaf, in Dobsonville near Soweto, specifically aimed at teachers who teach life skills to the Pre-School to Foundation Phase classes. This was very successful and we felt confident that the materials developed are age appropriate and well suited for the needs of the teacher and the Deaf learner.

Materials developed: The educator manual

- Explains the role of caregivers, learners and educators.
- Gives useful contact numbers such as HIV and AIDS organisations, substance abuse organisations and legal help.
- Explains how the unit plans and the learners activity books work.
- Includes suggested outcomes based assessment activities as well as the Revised National Curriculum Statements adapted for Deaf learners.
- The main section consists of 16–17 unit plans. Each unit plan in the educator manual covers the following areas:
    1. how to prepare to teach the unit
    2. introduction activity
    3. interaction and video activity
    4. learners' activities
    5. home-based activities
    6. summary of learning
    7. extension activity and assessment ideas
- At the end of the educator manual there is an English transcript of the videos used in the Phase.

Table 1: Summary of SLED learning materials and videos by Grade level

	Topics covered include	Educator manuals	Learners activity books and posters	Videos
Pre-school and Grade R	• Building self esteem and self confidence • Deaf and hearing culture • Friendship • Awareness of body image • Keeping healthy • Germs • What to do when you are sick and how to look after others • Keeping yourself and your world safe • What to do in an emergency	34 pages	18 pages 5 posters Artwork and layout by Deaf artists depicting Nomsa and her Deaf mother. Minimal written language.	There is one story on this video focusing on Nomsa, a Deaf four year old who stays with her Deaf mother. During the story she has a bath, plays games with her mother, helps her mother make soup, eats her breakfast, learns how to catch the mini-bus taxi, visits her sick hearing grandfather, teaches him some signs and looks at family photographs with him. The story takes place in Tembisa, a township outside Johannesburg.

	Topics covered include	Educator manuals	Learners activity books and posters	Videos
Foundation phase (Grades 1–3)	• How boys and girls are the same and different • Everyone is unique and special • My body is my own • Healthy living • Germs and viruses • Illnesses • Basic facts about HIV and AIDS • Looking after people who are sick • Coping with loss	36 pages	22 pages 5 posters Artwork and layout by Deaf artists depicting four Deaf friends in Grade 2 at a township school for the Deaf. Minimal written language.	There is one story divided into three parts. The story focuses on four characters, John, Mpho, Hasina and their teacher Kathy. John is the victim of bullying which leads to a nasty accident, but Hasina and Mpho rush to Kathy for help. Kathy uses universal precautions to care for John's wound until the school nurse arrives and takes John away. This leads to a classroom discussion and game about HIV and AIDS with fellow classmates and Kathy. The friends later visit John in the hostel with some presents to help him recover and some good advice.
Intermediate phase (Grades 4–6)	• Identifying your own strengths and weaknesses • The importance of family and friends • Respect for others • Coping with peer pressure and substance abuse • Accessing health and emergency services • Facts about HIV and AIDS My body is changing	42 pages	22 pages 5 posters Artwork and layout by Deaf artists depicting four Deaf friends in Grade 5 at a semi-rural school for the Deaf. There is much more written English in this workbook however it is Deaf- and age-appropriate.	There are two videos at this phase with two stories on each video. After each story there is a commentary by an older Deaf learner, Mpho, discussing the topics that the story is exploring. In 'Changing Rooms' we flash between the two boys and the two girls getting changed for swimming. In 'Behind the hostel' Iqshaan persuades Tumi to have a smoke but Sandra and Thandi catch them in the act and we find out that Sandra's grandmother is dying of lung cancer. In 'After the HIV and AIDS lesson' the four friends sort out the myths around HIV and AIDS. In 'Blind children at MY school?' while doing their homework, the four friends explore their feelings about other disabled learners and what to do if you are being touched in a way that is wrong.
Senior phase (Grades 7–9)	• Personal development • The role of significant others and developing relationships • Physical and emotional changes • Drugs, smoking and alcohol • Love, infatuation and sex • Rape • Commercial sex workers • HIV and AIDS in depth • HIV testing • Living positively with HIV • Living with loss • Setting goals • Deaf culture as part of a majority culture e.g. Xhosa culture	46 pages	34 pages 5 posters Artwork and layout by Deaf artists depicting four Deaf friends in the final years of school. The setting is urban. The written English at this phase is advanced however it remains Deaf- and age-appropriate.	There are two videos at this phase with two stories on each video. After each story there is a commentary by an older Deaf woman, Atiyah, discussing the topics that the story is exploring. In 'Being Me' while designing posters, the friends explore supporting Deaf-worthy causes, traditional circumcision, substance abuse, Deaf and hearing cultures and infatuation. In 'The Date' Simphiwe and Kate visit Sister Jeff at the family planning clinic and they learn about contraceptive methods, peer pressure and STIs. In 'Date Rape' Simphiwe and her older sister rush to help Kate after she has been raped. Together they go to the police station where they report the case. They then visit the doctor who administers the rape kit. Both these interactions have a preferred interpreter present. In ' My Mum has AIDS' Gary reveals that is mother's sickness is in fact AIDS and Thando reveals that he will go ahead with his Xhosa circumcision. Both boys are very supportive and Gary's way of looking after his mother is insightful and learned.

Preparation for the launch

Towards the end of 2003 we were also awarded the tender to prepare for the launch of the *Life Skills, HIV and AIDS Education for the Deaf Learner*. We had several meetings with the steering committee in preparation for the launch, which was planned for March 2004. The steering committee also viewed the Pre-School and Grade R, Foundation Phase and Intermediate Phase videos. All of their comments were highly favourable. The team started working on the transcriptions of the videos that would be included at the back of the educator manuals.

In June and August 2003, we concentrated on finalising the educator manuals and learners activity books for the Pre-School, Grade R and Foundation Phase. The educator manuals, the learners activity books and posters are specifically aimed at the Deaf learner and are the first materials of this kind purposely developed for the Deaf by the Deaf in Southern Africa if not the continent. They are language appropriate and are illustrated by Deaf artists who reflect the experiences of the South African Deaf community.

First workshops in schools for the Deaf

In September and November 2003, we had our first Life Skills training workshops in the Free State and the Eastern Cape then later in Kwa Zulu Natal. As the members of SLED have many years experience both behind the school desk and in front of it we realised that the best way to help teachers and Deaf learners to access these materials was to run workshops at schools for the Deaf throughout South Africa. We knew that it was important for teachers of the Deaf to see the materials working with their Deaf learners from their school. So far we have trained 671 people: 568 hearing and 103 Deaf. We have run 16 three-day workshops and taught representatives from 27 schools that have Deaf learners. We have run workshops in all the provinces except Gauteng and the Western Cape. The workshop programme consists of:

- Demonstration lessons using Deaf learners (Pre-School to FET) from the school taught by Deaf members of the SLED team.

- Smaller breakaway groups in SASL using the *Life Skills, HIV and AIDS Education for the Deaf Learner* materials.

- Games and videos to enhance learning.

There is a separate programme during the workshop for Deaf learners who receive additional training in life skills from the SLED team. When we leave each school we give the school the videos, the educator manuals, and the learners activity books and posters appropriate for the school population. Teachers, hostel parents, teaching assistants, support staff and local representatives attend the workshops from the various Departments of Education. Recently the Deaf auxiliary workers and other DeafSA provincial social workers have been attending the workshops.

The response

At the end of each workshop we asked participants, both teachers and learners, to give their feedback on the materials and the training. This feedback was written, spoken or signed. The response from Deaf learners and teachers has been overwhelmingly positive, and reflect how the materials are getting the appropriate information across. Deaf learners' comments include:

'At last I have something in my language that I can understand. The videos and books they are amazing. Now I know what this AIDS no I mean HIV *and* AIDS stuff is all about. Now I am just the same as them.'

'All the materials are great because helps us the learners to see everything in a real life DEAF situation.'

'We are so able to relate to the videos, this makes it easy for the teachers and now learning means something.'

And a Deaf teacher concurs: 'Wow I am impressed, this is the first time in Deaf history we have this. They are great.'

Hearing teachers of the Deaf also found the videos invaluable, particularly as they presented information they otherwise wouldn't have had access to.

'The workshop was unbelievable. I cannot believe what I learnt in just three days – you have given me skills that, as a hearing person I thought I would never be able to possess. It was all perfect and so professional.'

'I have been teaching the Deaf for over 13 years. What I learnt over these last few days has given me a complete new perspective and a renewed enthusiasm for teaching. I feel like a new teacher just starting again. Thank you so much.'

No negative comments were received. However there has been some frustration at schools who have not yet received the full set of materials from the Department of Health.

Official launch

Since January 2004 we have continued with our Life Skills training workshops at schools for the Deaf in KwaZulu Natal, North West Province, Northern Cape, Mpumalanga and Limpopo. The Minster of Health, Dr M. Tshabalala-Msimang, and the Minister of Education, Prof K. Asmal, officially launched this project in March at a high profile event in Eldorado Park. We were delighted with the response from the media and the general public and are justifiably proud of the *Life Skills, HIV and AIDS Education for the Deaf Learner - An Illustrative Programme.*

In May 2004 we were asked to adapt Grade 10 Life Orientation materials (HIV and AIDS) developed by the Gauteng Institute for Educational Development (GIED) to suit the needs of the schools for the Deaf. We submitted our SASL video script and material adaptations to the GIED in June. We chose Mountain Sanctuary Park in the Magaliesburg as the place where we would film and auditioned for the four main characters. We had a highly successful shoot over a long weekend in August.

What next?

We have not visited all the schools for the Deaf in South Africa because of bureaucractic issues between the provincial departments of Education in the Western Cape and Gauteng and the national Department of Health. As we have not yet run workshops in all the schools for the Deaf, we have not yet had the opportunity to revisit the schools for the Deaf where we have held workshops and distributed materials to the Deaf learners and the teachers. Once the project is completed, we will analyse its impact and review any changes. However, we had lots of positive feedback from our workshops across the country and from the pre-test given at selected schools in Gauteng and the Western Cape.

In April 2005 we held a national Life Skills, HIV and AIDS Education workshop for the social workers and Deaf auxiliary workers employed mainly by DeafSA. Although the materials were specifically developed for Deaf school learners we deliberately made the Senior Phase suitable for school learners and Deaf adults. DeafSA's social workers and Deaf auxiliary workers are very excited to have materials that are accessible for Deaf clients. The series of six videos have been distributed to all DeafSA's provincial offices and various other groups working with Deaf adults. However the social workers and Deaf auxiliary workers feel that they need additional training with the materials preferably on site in their various provincial offices.

As many of the schools for the Deaf in South Africa are boarding schools, we soon became aware of the important but neglected role that the caregivers play in the lives of the Deaf children in their care. These include hostel mothers, cooks, cleaners, and gardeners, often ex-pupils of the schools where they now work. Although in subsequent workshops we invited these caregivers to attend the workshop, many were not allowed to or unable to participate. The caregivers that we did work with were desperate for training, so we hope to do much more work with this population. Many of the schools for the Deaf take learners from isolated, rural areas. The parents of these learners are especially ignorant of SASL and what and how their Deaf children are learning. We are currently developing materials for this highly neglected group.

We also would like to train and distribute the materials in other southern African countries. Although the videos and illustrations are in SASL and take place in South African settings, the SASL used would be widely accessible and the settings are appropriate to many other neighbouring countries.

Conclusion

Life Skills, HIV and AIDS Education for the Deaf Learner — An Illustrative Programme was developed to build up a framework of understanding around HIV and AIDS for South African Deaf learners from an early age. It has proven to be highly popular among Deaf learners and their teachers. The learners are eager to watch the videos again and again as this is the first time that they have had mini-movies in their language describing their experiences. They also find the written and illustrated materials appropriate for their learning. At last they have the opportunity to access information around everything to do with life skills, from what a germ is to how to support someone living with HIV. As a South African Deaf organisation, concerned by our country's high AIDS figures, we are extremely confident that the first educational SASL materials for Deaf learners will go a long way towards preventing South Africa's Deaf youth adding to these statistics.

These materials are available from the South African National Department of Health:

Ms Nokuthula Prusent
Deputy Director – HIV, AIDS & TB Youth Programme
Department of Health
Private Bag X828,
Pretoria, South Africa, 0001
Tel: +27123120148
Fax: +27123123185
email: pruseN@health.gov.za

Notes

1. All learners in schools in South Africa follow the Revised National Curriculum Statement as devised by the national Department of Education. They have divided these statements up into different learning areas. These areas include Languages, Natural Sciences, Technology, Art and Culture and Life Orientation.

Contact information

Sign Language Education and Development – SLED
Western Cape
F403 66 Albert Road
Woodstock
7925 Cape Town, South Africa
Tel: +2721 448 2520
Fax: +2721 448 2520
email: info@sled.org.za

A message from Wangechi[1]: Confronting the perils of Deaf Kenyans in the face of HIV/AIDS

Kevin Henderson

Deaf Worlds
2006 | vol 22 (1)
Forest Books ©
ISSN 1362–3125

I was waiting for the bus with two other volunteers at a bustling bus station in Nairobi, when I suddenly saw her: Wangechi, my former student from Rongo. Because the little town of Rongo is quite a distance away from the big city of Nairobi – a full day's bus-ride – just bumping into someone I know there was unusual enough. However, to see someone looking so unlike the student I met and revered little more than two years earlier seemed surreal.

In the year 2000, I was Wangechi's teacher in Class 8 at the Kuja Primary School for the Deaf in Rongo town, Nyanza Province. I remember her name in Kenyan Sign Language (KSL) was a closed fist completing a circle on the forehead.[2] Always tidily dressed in her orange-white checkered school uniform, she had thick black hair that was neat and closely cropped and a beautiful wide, toothy smile.

It was my first year as her English teacher. One of my earliest and fondest memories of Wangechi was her not-so-simple transformation into the character of a belligerent goat for a class play that also had a cow, a sheep and a donkey. She wanted to be in the play but feared being laughed at. It wasn't easy to rehearse, but slowly she eased into her role. During the ensuing performance two weeks later in front of the whole school she was very animated and stood out with more confidence than I had ever seen in her. All the students laughed at the goat she portrayed and for several months after the play she happily accepted the fanfare with a smile. It became a lasting memory for me.

The next year I was her Math teacher, where I often had the students work together in groups at the board solving problems amidst clouds of chalk dust. From the often blank expression on her face I could tell it was not her favorite subject. She wasn't the ideal student – she didn't have high marks; she was an orphan who had already by the age of 13 had a baby out of wedlock – but I knew she was smart, very caring about others, and always wanted to do her best.

Wangechi mattered to me, and I remembered she was also someone important among her peers. Boys and girls alike respected her and listened to her whether she was serious or playful – they looked up to her as a friend and a 'sister'. When I finished my Peace Corps service, we had exchanged smiles and addresses but never wrote each other. I had returned to the U.S. with every hope for her future despite her loss of mother and father.

Fast-forward two years, when I had just returned to Kenya with a grant in one hand and a project blueprint in the other, determined to put a dent in the rising tide of HIV/AIDS through the "HIV Awareness Project of the Deaf". Waiting for the bus that would take the two volunteers and I on our first research trip for the project, I saw Wangechi walking up to me with a disheveled look alongside a young man who walked with a swagger and seemed high on something. In place of her clean, school uniform of the past were a pullover and blue jeans which weren't ragged but needed some washing. Her hair was shabby and her smile half-hearted. She couldn't seem to concentrate on me as her eyes darted left and right. Gone was the look of confidence I had worked so hard to instill in her. "Something is out of sorts," my gut was telling me. However, bumping into her at that time I felt as if I were receiving a message with very important information......that now seems almost prophetic.

Amidst constant interruption from the irritating, not-so-sober young man, I learned that Wangechi had completed training in cooking at the Karen Vocational Program for the Deaf in Nairobi, was looking for work, and wanted me to send her photos of my wife and baby, in that order. Then, as suddenly as she had appeared, she ran off again to await a different bus and left me to contend with the young man alone for a good half hour but with flittering images of her talking hands still dancing in the back of my mind. The message was delivered but the information wasn't yet clear to me.......

My understanding grew afterwards, through working and hanging out with the local Deaf community, and pumping hours and hours of the universal Deaf gossip-machine about current events and people. I learned that a young, married man had just passed away due to complications of HIV/AIDS. He not only left behind in his wake a Deaf wife with three children, but also dozens of women – hearing and deaf – infected with HIV. His wife continues to live free of HIV but in the case of Wangechi, the former student I revered, it was not so. Wangechi was one of his sex partners. I now recall with irony that, at the bus stop on that fateful day, Wangechi was entering none other than the bus designated for the neighborhood where that man resided. Most likely she was going to see him. He was well-known among the Deaf in Kenya, albeit notorious for his sexual exploits. I had bumped into her at the bus stop only weeks before her partner died and now I do not know of any way to contact her. I heard that she finally got work in a hoteli (a small restaurant) in a village near Lake Victoria – a full day's journey from Nairobi.

Learning all this about my former student reminds me that the "HIV Awareness Project of the Deaf" is only at the beginning of a very long journey and Wangechi, and others like her, are the heart of our journey. I remember that a few years ago, as a teacher given a syllabus of only basic subjects, I felt frustrated that so little time was available to focus on sexual health and hygiene as areas of education for my students. One week I was barely able to find a half hour to demonstrate how egg and sperm meet, and then the next week I found out a 'sugar daddy' – or pimp – had used a student in Class 7 for business in the wee hours over the weekend. It was obvious that the huge void of awareness and responsibility of sex and relationships among Deaf youth and adults needed serious improvements, but not with minute lessons at inconsistent intervals on top of a strenuous curriculum.

As a Deaf person, I was aware of the extra difficulties that a Deaf child faces while growing up, while trying to develop and express identity, while trying to fit into a world that operates differently. But for Deaf youth in a developing country, where the hearing section of the population is already being ravaged by the HIV epidemic, the lack of information, communication and coping skills becomes even more disastrous. Who would tell them? New Deaf-friendly voluntary counseling and testing services for the first time have just become available in Nairobi, Kisumu, and Mombasa but too few were aware and able to access them, let alone able to afford the travel fare. Most parents and teachers in Deaf schools struggle with sign language; too few of them are fluent in KSL, but even then, a lack of training and vocabulary makes them more uncomfortable in addressing issues pertaining to sexual health. In a mind-set of "This is enough; it has to change!" we put our heads together in an effort to develop and launch a new peer educator program by and for the Deaf.

After a successful research trip in late March 2004 in which many focus group discussions were conducted in three schools of the Deaf in west Kenya – Nyang'oma, Maseno, and Mumias – the first seeds of a peer educator network were planted. Four Deaf teachers, obviously held in high regard by their peers and students, were invited for training to become master educators (MEs) in April. Two weeks after completion of training, the MEs invited 40 top students from their schools to a peer education seminar later that month in Kisumu, a town on the shore of Lake Victoria brimming with bicycle taxis. The seminar was a success leaving the peer educators pining for more training.

Where before there was only a huge communication vacuum – the silent, flickering television set, the invisible radio, the indecipherable newspaper or the distant uncomfortable parent – now the project team and volunteers are together quickly creating and using new, Deaf-friendly activities and tools that encourage students to discuss and think critically about health and responsibility, including accessing VCT (voluntary counseling and testing) services for the Deaf, and that would even benefit those who can hear. Word quickly got around in surrounding schools about the project and a buzz grew so that other schools and their headmasters and teachers throughout the country have started calling upon us to visit and implement peer education programs to enhance HIV/AIDS awareness. Too many teachers, school staff, and students are experiencing firsthand the impact of the

HIV/AIDS epidemic. One can easily sense the starving among them for a solution to their predicament, the need for communication tools to address such issues. In addition, we are helping Deaf persons with access to Deaf-friendly voluntary counseling and testing services and treatment programs.

Now with the project underway, things are still far from rosy, and others like Wangechi are there to remind us so. Even at full throttle, the project is overshadowed by the giant behemoth that is Deaf people's lack of awareness and access to health services. Despite obstacles, progress is made one step at a time. We continue the journey, our goals firmly in sight.

As for Wangechi, I have not forgotten her. While it may not be possible for me to reach her directly, I hope to reach her through the many Deaf people the project aims to help. The program is now creating the seedlings of a corps of leadership and awareness. Together, these sprouts can gradually break through the concrete wall of silence and ignorance, to reach and inspire more Deaf people. Such efforts may eventually reach and re-instill confidence and health in Wangechi. Our project is dedicated to Wangechi, the heart of our journey.

Notes

1. This name is not the real name and has been changed for purposes of confidentiality.
2. This sign name – the most common form of nomenclature used in the deaf community – is not her true name and has been changed for purposes of confidentiality.

Acknowledgments

I thank my dear friends of the Deaf community of Kenya and abroad, Tom Mbanda Ger, Laura Chertkow, Koen Van Rompay, Allison Pohl, and the volunteers and staff of Sahaya International. This program was funded by a grant of the Development Marketplace program of the World Bank to Sahaya International.

Short report of Liverpool VCT and Care (LVCT) work in progress

Kevin Henderson

Deaf Worlds
2006 | vol 22 (1)
Forest Books ©
ISSN 1362–3125

Key words

Deaf culture, HIV/AIDS, Deafness, Kenya, barriers to information, sexual health

Abstract

Today the local Kenyan Deaf community receives Deaf-friendly voluntary counselling and testing (VCT) services for free in three urban, integrated VCT sites (Nairobi, Mombasa, Kisumu) thanks to pioneering efforts by Liverpool VCT (LVCT) since 2003. The overall mission of the LVCT organization's outreach programme is to reduce transmission of HIV and other sexually-transmitted diseases in local Kenyan Deaf communities.

Biography

Kevin Henderson is from California, USA, and is a Deaf activist and educator. He wrote this article when he worked as project director for the "HIV Awareness Project of the Deaf" of Sahaya International in Nairobi, Kenya. He currently works as the Deaf HIV/AIDS Program and Conferences coordinator for the Liverpool VCT & Care organization in Nairobi.

Background

In conjunction with local stakeholders, the three integrated VCT sites were founded by LVCT for the local Deaf community in Kenya, which numbers around 87,000 (Nyang'aya, 1998), as well as the general public. Each site employs Deaf counselors and peer educators as well as a hearing counselor fluent in Kenyan Sign Language.

Through these services, a Deaf person is able to voluntarily receive pre- and post-test counseling and find out his/her HIV status. Also, with the provision of a hearing counselor, each site is able to cater to hearing clientele willing to pay a fee. Should the client test positive for HIV, the counselor refers her/him to a care program at the main LVCT office in Nairobi or at local hospitals in Kisumu and Mombasa.

Among the 150 VCT sites throughout Kenya for which LVCT has provided training, technical assistance, and support, the three catering to the Deaf community are Nyaweri Deaf VCT, launched Dec 9, 2004 in Kisumu, bordering Lake Victoria; the Nairobi Deaf VCT, launched on Feb 14, 2004 in Buruburu (now situated in downtown Nairobi); and the Coast Deaf VCT, launched in Mombasa in July 2004. Reportedly the first of their kind in East Africa and abroad as pilot models without precedent (Muganda, 2004), the Deaf VCT sites also conduct peer education and mobile VCT activities spanning urban regions into rural settings and hard-to-reach Deaf clientele without money for transport.

Challenges

Following discovery of a positive HIV status in a Deaf person, access to health and life-sustaining treatment, already scant, is further obstructed by obstacles such as the lack of communication and sensitivity by the referral care staff. Furthermore, the quality of service is weakened by the lack of a professional interpreter training institution in Kenya, as use of informal sign language interpreters compromises confidentiality and anonymity. Without sensitive communication and accommodation, services are ineffective and impractical and the Deaf client becomes less willing to continue adherence towards a longer, healthy life.

Methods

To address these gaps, LVCT began a pilot peer-support group for Deaf people living with HIV/AIDS (DPLWHA) in the Nairobi region in August, 2005. At monthly meetings facilitated by a Deaf professional, ways of maintaining health and care will be covered as well as means of improving relations between hearing professionals and Deaf participants. After one year of peer-support meetings two more groups will be established (in Mombasa and Kisumu) to cater to the Deaf clientele in those regions. Input collected from these meetings will foster development of a better care and support program for DPLWHA at VCT and care facilities in LVCT, hospitals, and clinics.

Since early 2004, mobile VCT clinics conducted by Deaf peer educators have been concentrated in the rural areas of Central province and Nairobi area. However, as of May 2005, mobile VCT activities were expanded to rural areas surrounding Kisumu such as Homa Bay where the Luo people are most numerous. The Swahili city of Mombasa, on the coast, and its environs followed in July 2005. Due to tireless efforts – for example, walking on foot all day from home to home (in place of the standard megaphone for those who can hear) – of peer educators, more Deaf people benefit from VCT services. Before the counselors can conduct VCT services in a rural Deaf community, the peer educators take steps to secure permission and ensure DPLWHA in outreach areas can access a care facility in their vicinity. Still, many more hard-to-reach Deaf people do not know about VCT services.

There are some ways to change that. Thanks to increasing access of technology, news of mobile VCT activities coming to a specific community can be received by Deaf Kenyans nationally via mobile phone text messages. Also, a professional Deaf puppetry troupe is being enlisted to promote mobile VCT activities in Kenyan Sign Language. Action like this shall bring more VCT services to the Deaf community, nonetheless more creative ways are still needed to support this action.

Ownership of sexual and reproductive health services by local Deaf organizations and stakeholders is vitally relevant to the Deaf community's access to such services. LVCT recognizes the need for Deaf ownership and solidarity and has plans underway for inviting Deaf organizations to capacity building workshops. By instructing them on organization and personnel management, accounting, and fund-raising, LVCT aims to pass the reins of each Deaf VCT to a local Deaf organization in two years. For example, the Nyaweri Deaf VCT (see Adoyo, this volume), with its board members representing **Nyanza, Western,** and **Rift** Valley provinces, is currently ironing out its constitution and securing community-based organization (CBO) registration with the local government. With LVCT capacity building activities, the Nyaweri Deaf VCT Support Development Group will be able to manage and sustain the Deaf VCT.

Conclusion

Many challenges lie ahead of LVCT in our effort to alleviate the dearth of sexual and reproductive health services for the Kenyan Deaf community and abroad. Based on anecdotal accounts from Deaf people passing through Kenya from neighboring countries like the Democratic Republic of Congo, Rwanda, and Uganda, many Deaf people are unaware of their HIV status and unknowingly pass HIV among each other and outside the community. A regional as well as international forum needs to be established to discuss ways of reducing HIV transmission among the Deaf on a wider scale. Popular literature and research on HIV/AIDS/STIs still ignores the special needs of the Deaf, leaving them in the dark.

References

Adoyo, P. O. (this volume). A report on the Nyaweri HIV/AIDS Awareness Project of the Deaf in Kenya.

Muganda, C. (2004, April 7). Inside a VCT Centre for the Deaf. *Daily Nation.* Retrieved July 10, 2005, from http://www.deaftoday.com/news/archives/004353.html

Nyang'aya, D. (1998, May). Addressing special populations. Forgotten: A view of the social and political obstacles to the prevention and treatment of AIDS in Kenyan deaf people. *African Link*, 20-22.

Contact information

Kevin Henderson
PO Box 1949 00100
Nairobi
Kenya
email: kkhender@yahoo.com

A report on the Nyaweri HIV/AIDS Awareness Project of the Deaf in Kenya

Peter Oracha Adoyo

 Deaf Worlds
2006 | vol 22 (1)
Forest Books ©
ISSN 1362–3125

Key words

HIV/AIDS, Kenyan deaf community, voluntary counseling and testing, Kenyan Sing Language, intervention strategies, Nyaweri VCT Centre

Biography

Peter Oracha Adoyo is a trained teacher for the deaf. He did his postgraduate studies at the Centre for Deaf Studies, University of Bristol, UK, and has a Ph.D. in Deaf Education from the University of Hamburg, Germany. He is currently a lecturer and the chair of the Department of Special Education at Maseno University, Kenya.

Introduction

The HIV/AIDS data in Kenya is alarming. There are about 1.4 million infected women, 900,000 men and 220,000 children. About 1.5 million currently require care and treatment. There is an HIV prevalence rate of 30% in most districts in Kenya (Bururia, 2003, p. 14). The situation is gloomy as the disease has no cure, and it is estimated that 500–700 of those who have developed AIDS die daily. Although it is widely held that 90% of Kenyans are aware of HIV/AIDS, this is not true. Knowledge of the symptoms, prevalence, and methods of infection, prevention and care of the sick is still lacking, especially in the rural areas. Indeed the sick are still stigmatized, isolated and abandoned.

While the epidemiological impact has been significant, the corresponding impact on the social welfare of the family has been devastating. Decades of improvement in social welfare have been undermined by the inhabited progression of the epidemic. The imbalance in household structure, with women and children forming the majority of dwellers, has worsened. Children have been pulled into the informal economy to supplement income lost when their parents become sick or die of AIDS or related illnesses.

Economic legal and social equalities have particularly placed women in a vulnerable position in preventing HIV transmission, while at the same time making them more responsible and less able to respond to family illness and losses due to AIDS. Families and communities have felt the greatest burden of AIDS and need assistance as they cope with its impact. The impact of AIDS on the family has resulted in a rising number of orphans. Most of these children have been absorbed into the extended families and are cared for by relatives including grandparents. Others are cared for by siblings and a sizable number have found a home in the street.

HIV/AIDS has also played a key role in decimating health care facilities. Many health care facilities have been overburdened by an increasing demand for services and decreasing resources. While home based care is being advocated within the existing heath system, there is a lack of resources to provide training and follow up to the thousands of families trying to care for sick family members at home (Rau, Forsythe & Okeyo, 1996).

The deaf community and HIV/AIDS

In 2003, the Kenya National Association of the Deaf (KNAD) realized that many deaf people were dying of AIDS. Even though the government, through the National Aids Control Council, boosted its HIV/AIDS awareness efforts aimed at behavior and attitude change through the media, such as radio and television, this information did not reach the deaf community. This is due to the fact that these information campaigns use spoken and written language which is difficult for deaf people to access. It was realized that this lack of appropriate communication would have a negative effect on the prevention and management of the disease and that it would have a devastating impact on the survival of the deaf community. We therefore had to intervene.

In March 2003, we started a project, which would coordinate HIV/AIDS activities in this region. The project was named Nyaweri. The acronym NYA-WE-RI stands for **Nya**nza, **We**stern and **Ri**ft Valley provincial regions as shown in the map.

Map of Kenya's provincial regions (Source: Kenya Institute of Education, 1991, p. 4)

The estimated number of deaf people in these three provinces, the provinces covered by our project, is about 30,000. The objective was and is still to create HIV/AIDS awareness amongst the members of the deaf community. The first step we took was to look for funds to train members of the deaf community on the prevention and management of the disease using a communication method that could be understood by the community, i.e. Kenyan Sign Language. We were aware that training a big group for only one week would not achieve much, but we hoped that the regular training on the focus groups already created by the Kenya National Association for the Deaf were likely to cover the area pretty well and could offer a good chance of supervision. Consequently we set out the following objectives:

• To hold a one-week training of trainers workshop for deaf youths on the symptoms, prevalence, methods of infection, and prevention of HIV/AIDS, using Kenyan Sign Language as the language of information delivery.

- To use the deaf trainees to create awareness among the deaf communities on the realities of HIV/AIDS through campaigns and community mobilization in order to curtail the spread of HIV/AIDS among deaf members.

- To offer effective and quality Voluntary Counseling and Testing (VCT) of HIV/AIDS services to the deaf community by setting up a VCT center for the deaf in this region.

- To provide home-based care services and enhance the quality of life of the deaf members who are HIV positive or have developed AIDS.

- To establish a community computerized health information and sign language programme on HIV/AIDS for the deaf community.

- To collaborate with the relevant stakeholders and partners through networking to fight the HIV/AIDS scourge in the deaf community.

The first training session (phase one) of the project took place in November 2003 at the Maseno School for the Deaf. It was funded by De Gelderhorst, an organization of elderly deaf people based in the Netherlands. It involved the following activities:

- Identification of ten intelligent, literate deaf youths with an open-minded attitude towards HIV/AIDS.

- Identification of reknown facilitators on HIV/AIDS.

- Identification of three competent Kenyan Sign Language interpreters to interpret during the workshop.

- Carrying out the workshop.

The one-week workshop was very interactive with open discussions on HIV/AIDS myths and realities. All the workshop proceedings were interpreted to the deaf trainees in Kenyan Sign Language while handouts were also provided. The facilitators used video clips with HIV/AIDS themes to provide the participants with additional information.

The second phase of the project, which took place from February to June 2004, was financially supported by Maurice and Suzette Gosschalk from Rotterdam, Holland.[1] This phase involved dissemination of HIV/AIDS information to the deaf community. Using the deaf trainees, we moved out to the regional focus groups for the deaf and schools for the deaf located in different parts of the provinces. These visits were very successful as we employed a participatory and interactive approach using Kenyan Sign Language to create HIV/AIDS awareness.

Achieving the third goal, i.e. setting up a VCT center for the deaf took some time because we did not have funds ready to set up a center. However in July 2004, we approached a local NGO, Liverpool VCT, which coordinated various HIV/AIDS voluntary counseling and testing projects in Kenya (see Henderson, this volume) and requested their support. They accepted our proposal and agreed to support us.

Because the deaf personnel working at the center had to be trained first, Liverpool VCT organized an intensive one-month training on HIV/AIDS counseling, testing and on community mobilization for the ten trained deaf members of the group in June 2004. It was after this training that they set up a Voluntary Counseling and Testing center for the deaf in Kisumu, which we named Nyaweri VCT for the Deaf.

Nyaweri VCT for the Deaf

This center has been operational since November 2004. It has four deaf staff members who work full time, i.e. two counselors and two community mobilizers, who go out to the community to discuss HIV/AIDS related issues and to give advice particularly on the advantages of visiting the VCT center. There is also an interpreter attached to the center to cater for the needs of hearing clients. He works on a part time basis. All are employed by Liverpool VCT.

Other community mobilizers are working in the field. The role of the community mobilizers is to go out into the community and discuss HIV/AIDS related issues and to advice them on the advantages of visiting the VCT center.

Achievements and success indicators

- We have completed Phase 1 of the training of trainers for ten deaf youths on HIV and AID awareness in the deaf community.

- We are conducting HIV/AIDS awareness and AIDS prevention and family life education for the deaf in the region. This activity is ongoing.

- With the assistance of Liverpool VCT, we organized a one-month training for ten deaf youths on HIV/AIDS counseling, testing, and community mobilization.

- With the support of Liverpool VCT we established the Nyaweri VCT center for the deaf in Kisumu. Many deaf people visit this center to find out their HIV status.

- We have increased capacity building for the counseling of infected, affected, families and the deaf community in general.

There is now an increasing general awareness of the existence of the HIV/AIDS epidemic in the deaf community. There is a gradual reduction in the number of deaths resulting from HIV/AIDS in the deaf community since the start of the programme. We have also noted a decrease in the number of deaf members being infected and affected by AIDS.

In general, there is a better understanding of choice through VCT advisory services. Our survey also shows that safer sex methods including condom use, abstinence, and other behaviour changes have been adopted.

Future plans and challenges

In the near future, we are planning to organise training for home-based care for the deaf community members who are bed ridden. We also want to organise a workshop for capacity building for the Nyaweri board members. Finally, we are planning to start peer education for the deaf community on HIV/AIDS. Meanwhile, Liverpool VCT has notified the Nyaweri board members that they will soon be handing over the project. Therefore, the board will have to think of the project's sustainability.

Presently, our project covers a very wide area because there is only one VCT center at Kisumu. There is need for other VCT centers, at least one in each province, in order to cater for the needs of all the community members. Although we are trying to reach distant areas through the mobile VCT, it has been very difficult since we still do not have a project vehicle. Most of the time, our staff have to walk long distances to reach the community members. We need a vehicle to help us carry out the mobile VCT effectively.

There are a number of deaf people who are now down with AIDS and who require home-based care services. This is not possible because our staff have not yet been trained in this area but would require the necessary skills if they worked as counselors. We also need funds to buy anti-retroviral drugs for the infected to prolong their lives. Currently, there is no computerized health information system because of lack of funds. We continue to look for money to create one.

HIV/AIDS is highly related to poverty. Because most members of the deaf community have no jobs and are generally poor, they remain vulnerable to the disease. We have to look for ways and means of empowering the deaf community financially. This, however, is a long-term objective.

Generally, the deaf community is happy that this project has taken off. The deaf communities that have been visited to date are now able to discuss HIV/AIDS issues without shame. Apart from the challenges, which must always be there, the project has shown its first positive impact on the community.

Notes

1. The couple had been introduced to us by their daughter, Dr. Renee Heinneman-Gosschalk, who had worked at the Maseno School for the Deaf some years back.

References

Bururia, S. (2003, October 2). What needs to be done on HIV/AIDS. *East African Standard*, 14.

Henderson, K. (this volume). Short report of Liverpool VCT and Care (LVCT) work in progress.

Kenya Institute of Education. (1991). *GHC pupils book 4: Our province – Nyanza*. Nairobi: Jomo Kenyatta Foundation.

Rau, B., Forsythe, S., & Okeyo, T. (1996). An introduction to Kenyan's epidemic. In B. Rau & S. Forsyth (Eds.), *AIDS in Kenya: Socioeconomic impact and policy implications*. Nairobi: Family Health International/ AIDSCAP. 1–10.

Contact information

Peter Oracha Adoyo, Ph.D.
email: poracha@hotmail.com and Poracha@yahoo.com

The first HIV/AIDS education project for deaf people in The Gambia

Constanze Schmaling and Dodou Loum

Deaf Worlds
2006 | vol 22 (1)
Forest Books ©
ISSN 1362–3125

Key words

HIV/AIDS, deafness, Gambia, Gambian Sign Language, deaf community/deaf association, sexual education

Abstract

In September/October 2004, the Gambian Association of Deaf and Hard of Hearing People (GADHOH) conducted a small HIV/AIDS education project in the greater Banjul area with the aim to teach deaf and hard of hearing people in The Gambia about HIV/AIDS. This was the first time that a project of this type was conducted within the deaf community in The Gambia. The project activities included the training of deaf trainers, a workshop for deaf members as well as an HIV/AIDS drama play. All participants responded very positively to this first HIV/AIDS education programme. The teaching materials developed by GAHDOH for this project are kept for future use. GADHOH hopes that they will be able to extend their services to the provinces and that the Gambian National AIDS Secretariat (NAS) will continue to support this type of education programme.

Biographies

Constanze Schmaling has a Ph.D. in sign language linguistics from the University of Hamburg and has worked in Africa since 1988. She has collaborated with GADHOH for the past five years as a member of the EdDev team.

Dodou Loum is the Managing Director of GADHOH and was responsible for the successful realisation of the AIDS education project.

Introduction

In September/October 2004, GADHOH, the Gambian Association of Deaf and Hard of Hearing People, conducted a small HIV/AIDS education project in the greater Banjul area. The aim of the project was to provide deaf and hard of hearing people in The Gambia with detailed information on HIV/AIDS, to teach them how they can protect themselves and other people from getting the virus, and to give them information on how to assist victims of the deadly disease. This was the first time that a project of this type was conducted within the deaf community in The Gambia.

Map of The Gambia (Source: CIA, 2005)

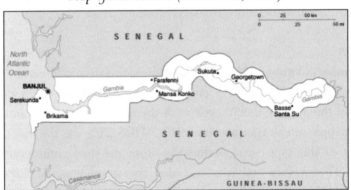

GADHOH is a registered non-governmental organisation that was founded in 1992 and became a member of the World Federation of the Deaf in 1994. GADHOH is working for the creation of a society in which deaf and hard of hearing people participate fully as citizens of the nation and enjoy all the benefits of such citizenship on a fair and equal basis. Its major activities include the development of a national sign language, teacher training, interpreter training and sign language courses.[1] The association also provides employment finding services for its members, literacy training for deaf adults, skill training for young deaf women as well as pre-school education for deaf children. It is also engaged in awareness campaigns to inform the public about the needs of deaf people and aims at a nation-wide membership to enable all deaf Gambians to participate in the organisation to facilitate improvement of their living conditions. In January 2006, GADHOH had 490 registered deaf and hard of hearing ordinary members.

EdDev (Education for Development), a UK-based organisation, which has been collaborating with GADHOH for the past five years in the successful implementation of the above activities, assisted the association in submitting an application for financial support to the National AIDS Secretariat (NAS) in order to make this project possible. EdDev is also involved in the evaluation of the project.

There are highly varying statistics on the number of deaf and hard of hearing people in The Gambia. The UNICEF National Disability Survey of The Gambia in 1998 (UNICEF, 1998) gives an incidence of deaf people as 1.1 per 1,000 in the population and for hard of hearing people as 1.9 per 1,000. This would imply that there are approximately 5,000 deaf and hard of hearing people in the total population of approximately 1.59 million people[2]. According to The World Federation of the Deaf (WFD) the number of deaf people is about one in nine of the total population (this includes all types of hearing loss).[3] Applied to The Gambia this would mean that there are approximately 175,000 deaf and hard of hearing people. However, there have been no studies in The Gambia to confirm these figures.

The HIV/AIDS education project

The first case of AIDS in The Gambia was identified in 1986. According to the Medical and Health Department in The Gambia and to information from the WHO, HIV/AIDS related sicknesses and deaths in The Gambia are increasing at an alarming rate and no section of the population is immune. For 2003, UNAIDS quoted an HIV prevalence rate of 1.2%, with an estimate of 6,800 HIV-positive persons (approx. 6,300 adults and 500 children) and 600 deaths as a result of the virus.[4] According to information from the NAS office at the Medical and Health Department in Banjul, the latest survey on the state of the epidemic in The Gambia, conducted in 2003, indicates that 2.1% of the population are infected with the virus; this would amount to approximately 26,000 people infected with HIV. However, the vast majority do not know their status.[5] There are no statistics on the number of HIV infected Deaf people. However, analysis of some results from public testing sites in the U.S. showed that the HIV infection rate among the Deaf population was two to ten times more than that of the surrounding hearing population (Monaghan, this volume; cf. Van Biema, 1994).

Since there is no cure for HIV/AIDS and drugs are not easily available and very costly, the only weapon to fight the spread of HIV/AIDS is information and education. There are awareness campaigns both by the government and by non-governmental organisations in various parts of the country, mainly through the mass media and through educational materials.

AIDS poster on Banjul's streets
(photograph taken in March 2004 by Constanze Schmaling)

Deaf people have limited access to this information as it is presented either in spoken or written language, even if the written information is given in one of the Gambian languages[6] (and not in English) as it is usually in a much higher-grade level language and contains vocabulary not easily understood by deaf people. The communication barrier is also present in the medical setting: health care providers usually have no sign language knowledge, and the training of sign language interpreters in The Gambia has only recently begun. It is therefore vital to provide access to information and health education and prevention programmes for Deaf people in their own language, Gambian Sign Language, and through visual media and visual teaching aids.

It is against this background that GADHOH decided to carry out an HIV/AIDS education project. The project took place in the greater Banjul area where most of the association's members live. The project was financially supported by the NAS who paid for approximately two thirds of the costs while GADHOH took the responsibility for the other third of expenses.

Project activities

The project activities started with the recruitment of 17 deaf people (eight women and nine men) for a three-day drama rehearsal. This was followed by a two-day training of trainers workshop. After this, preparation for training other GADHOH members at the three training centres began where each group was taught for three days each in succession.

Training of trainers

The training of trainers workshop lasted for two days. The participants of this workshop were all members of GADHOH staff and included the executive director, the director of the female wing, the six sign language tutors, and the association's artist. One non-staff GADHOH member also participated in the workshop.

The NAS assisted by sending two of their staff specialised on HIV/AIDS: Mr. Kebba Kinteh of the Brikama Health Centre and Mr. Lamin Gassama, the divisional AIDS Coordinator Western Division. In addition to their training, they also provided various information materials, such as leaflets, cards, and books as well as contraceptives. Communication between the two hearing instructors and their deaf audience was facilitated through GADHOH's four interpreters who were all present during the trainers' workshop.

On the first day, Mr. Kinteh and Mr. Gassama gave a general introduction about the spread of the HIV/AIDS virus in the world in general, quoting from statistics of the WHO, and on the spread of the disease in The Gambia in particular. They then explained what HIV/AIDS is, focussing on the following topics and questions: How is the virus transmitted? How can a person protect her/himself from getting infected? What factors contribute to the spread of the virus? What are the symptoms of HIV/AIDS? What happens to a person who has contracted the virus? How can one assist people who are HIV-positive or have AIDS? Scientific details on the nature of the HIV virus were not part of the workshop as most participants had no background education on biology, anatomy, and physiology.

The second day started with a show of the video 'The Silent Epidemic' (1998) which was produced in Kenya. The video is divided into different sections which include information on sexually transmitted diseases, the need to use condoms during sexual intercourse as well as the importance of effective counselling. The part that particularly attracted the attention of the workshop participants showed terrible pictures of the effect of HIV/AIDS on the human body at the various stages of the disease.

The remainder of the day was spent with a continuation of explanations and discussions on the above-mentioned topics. The instructors also explained the meaning of Safer Sex and demonstrated the use of condoms.

At the end of the workshop, the sign language tutors each gave a brief summary of what they had learned about the HIV/AIDS virus. It was amazing to see how much information they had acquired during the workshop.

Training of GADHOH members

For the training of GADHOH members, the six sign language tutors were divided into three teams, and each team was attached to one of the three GADHOH training centres – Latrikunda, Brikama and Kanifing. Radio announcements were made appealing to families to let their deaf family members attend the training at the nearest centre. Notifications were also written to all members. The response at each centre was overwhelming.

Three days of training were organised at each centre. There were between 16 and 57 participants at each centre with as many female as male participants. While the number of participants remained fairly constant during the three days at Latrikunda (between 16 and 20) and Brikama (between 32 and 38), the number of dropouts at Kanifing was quite significant: while 57 people attended the workshop on the first day, only 41 were left on the third day. This was attributed to the fact that a lot of participants were shocked and frightened after watching the 'Silent Epidemic' video, in particular the section showing the effect of HIV/AIDS on the human body.

The first day at each centre began with a video show of 'The Silent Epidemic'. At the end of the video, the groups broke up into private discussions about what they had seen. Afterwards, the tutors began giving information about the HIV/AIDS virus, and participants were encouraged to ask questions at all times. The main focus of the teachers was on explaining the common causes of contracting and transmitting the virus – through blood-to-blood contact, blood transfusion and unprotected sexual intercourse – and ways to avoid being infected, e.g. by not sharing needles, knives, razor blades and toothbrushes, and by practising Safer Sex. They also demonstrated the proper use of condoms.

Prior to the three days training, most GADHOH members had information of HIV/AIDS in bits and pieces. The workshop helped to put these pieces together and to produce a clearer picture. Participants expressed their satisfaction at what they had learned. One student explained: "My friend always gave me one or two condoms whenever he passed by and advised me to always use them. But when I tried to wear it, it kept coming off, and I felt shy to ask for help. Now I am happy. I know how to do it." Two participants discussed the use of sterile instruments at the hospitals, and one said: "I won't allow any medical person to treat me with needles and blades if I know that the same tools have been used on someone else."

One exciting result of this project was that after the training participants were seen advising hearing members of their families, especially their younger brothers and sisters, and also their friends on the dangers of sexual promiscuity and related issues.

Drama play

Drama is an important tool for deaf education as most of the messages it tries to convey reaches the audience through the visual channel. It was therefore decided to develop a drama play on HIV/AIDS.

The story for the play was developed by four of the GADHOH sign language tutors and was based on their own (limited) knowledge about the HIV/AIDS virus. Some of the information they had on HIV was from a drama programme on national TV by the Gambia Family Planning Association and the NAS. Three other deaf people helped in developing the plot, and they also offered assistance during the rehearsals.

Participants of the drama group were picked by the sign language tutors who have the closest contact with the GADHOH members. The criteria for selection were the ability to sign, dance and act in public; female participation was also found to be essential.

In this particular play, a married man with a loving and dedicated wife and two school-age children gets infected with HIV as a result of his carefree lifestyle: he often makes excuses to get away from his family to pick up young prostitutes. When the first signs of AIDS begin to appear and he finds out about his positive status, his wife gets trained to nurse him. His family cares for him until he dies. The drama also shows that his wife and his other sexual partners are now also likely to contract the virus.[7]

This 45 minute drama play was intended purely for a deaf and hard of hearing audience and was staged at the Kanifing and Latrikunda centres. Originally, it was planned to only perform the drama in order to produce a videotape which could serve as information material for future HIV/AIDS education programmes in the provinces. However, as the workshop participants really wanted to watch the drama, it was decided to also have live performances.

Results and outlook

This first HIV/AIDS education programme was a full success. The intended outcome that deaf people become aware of the danger of this incurable disease was achieved. Participants of both the trainers' and the GADHOH members' workshops expressed their satisfaction about having gained a lot of new information about the HIV/AIDS virus. One of the students concluded: "People talk, talk about AIDS everyday. I was afraid to go out at night, thinking AIDS would attack me in the darkness, and I didn't know its hideout. OOH! How false! I know AIDS now and I am not afraid anymore."

The most obvious result of the workshop was an increase in awareness and changes in practices. The demand for condoms increased, and the "stick-to-one-partner"-slogan became commonly known and used among deaf people. Some young deaf women who were in the habit of frequently making new boyfriends became scared as they were pointed at during Deaf Club meetings and were advised by their deaf friends to abandon the practice. When going to the doctor or to the hospital deaf people now make sure that they are treated with sterilised needles and instruments.

The workshop showed that it is vital that HIV/AIDS education for deaf people needs to be carried out in sign language. Showing a video or staging a drama play prior to the teaching facilitates the participants' understanding of the disease. Even though the 'Silent Epidemic' video frightened some of the participants it was decided that it would be used in future workshops as well as it is important to show the devastating effects of the disease on the human body. In future workshops, participants will get information on the content of the video prior to seeing it in order to know what to expect.

GADHOH plans to develop a full HIV/AIDS education programme. The drama team will undergo further training. With their increased knowledge of HIV/AIDS, the team will develop new plays concentrating on the discrimination faced by HIV/AIDS patients and on the care of deaf patients infected by the virus. GADHOH is also planning to extend their education services to deaf people in the three regional branches Soma, Farafenni and Barra. The videotapes of the drama plays, the 'Silent Epidemic' video as well as the artistic drawings developed by this project will be used for this purpose as this will be a cost-effective way of training deaf people in the provinces: The training could be carried out by the tutors and there would be no need to travel with a drama group of 17 people. It is hoped that the NAS will continue to rely on GADHOH for its service to the country's deaf community.

AIDS teaching materials prepared by the NAS office that were used for the training

Notes

1. Documentation of the Gambian Sign Language has begun, and the first four sign language booklets have been published (GADHOH, 2002–2005). The compilation of a sign language dictionary is underway.
2. This is the CIA world factbook estimate for July 2005 (CIA, 2005).
3. Information obtained from the WFD, p.c., August, 2005. The WFD estimates that there are about 70 million deaf and hard of hearing people in the world.
4. These figures are from the UNAIDS 2004 report on HIV/AIDS (UNAIDS, 2004a and b) and from UNAIDS/WHO (2004). Adults in the report are defined as women and men aged 15 to 49.
5. Information obtained from Mr. Omar Dibba at the NAS office in Banjul, p.c., May 2005.
6. Mandinka, Wolof, Fula, to mention the most important ones.
7. A second plot was developed in which HIV/AIDS is pictured as a dangerous wild beast that is attacking powerless villagers and killing them. The villagers vow to retaliate. They form a militia and go into the bush to hunt the beast. When they find it, they attack it with guns, cutlasses, axes, and knives, praying and singing songs of revenge. After a severe fight, during which praise singers are beating drums and encouraging the militiamen to attack, the beast is finally killed. The villagers are excited and surround the beast, shouting "AIDS is dead, we are now free". This play was not performed as there wasn't sufficient time for rehearsal.

References

CIA. (2005). *The world factbook: The Gambia*. Retrieved January 15, 2006, from http://www.cia.gov/cia/publications/factbook/geos/ga.html

GADHOH. (2002–2005). *Gambian Sign Language: Books 1–4*. Banjul: Gambian Association of the Deaf and Hard of Hearing.

Groce, N. (April 2004). *Global survey on HIV/AIDS and disability*. Retrieved April 15, 2005, from http://cira.med.yale.edu/globalsurvey/

Monaghan, L. (this volume). Maryland 2003 HIV infection statistics for hearing and Deaf populations: Analysis and policy suggestions.

The silent epidemic. (1998). Nairobi: Ace Communications. (video).

UNAIDS. (2004a). *Report on the global HIV/AIDS epidemic, July 2004.* Retrieved April 15, 2005, from http://www.unaids.org/bangkok2004/report.html

UNAIDS. (2004b). *AIDS epidemic update, December 2004.* Retrieved April 15, 2005, from http://www.unaids.org/wad2004/report.html

UNAIDS/WHO. (2004). *Epidemiological Fact Sheet 2004: The Gambia.* Retrieved April 15, 2005, from http://www.childinfo.org/eddb/hiv_aids/factsheets/pdfs/Gambia_en.pdf

UNICEF. (1998). *National disability survey of The Gambia.* UNICEF.

Van Biema, D. (1994, April 4). AIDS and the Deaf. *Time Magazine, 143 (14),* 76-77.

Contact information
Dodou Loum
Managing Director
GADHOH
P.O. Box 1518
Banjul
The Gambia
email: gadhoh@yahoo.com
Constanze Schmaling, Ph.D.
email: constanze.schmaling@t-online.de

Deaf People and HIV/AIDS in Ethiopia[1]

Alemayehu Teferi

Deaf Worlds
2006 | vol 22 (1)
Forest Books ©
ISSN 1362–3125

Key words

HIV/AIDS, deafness, Ethiopia, health statistics, infection rates

Biography

Alemayehu Teferi who became deaf at the age of 15 due to meningitis, earned a first class degree in economics at Addis Ababa University. In 1996, he became the chairman of the Ethiopian National Association of the Deaf (ENAD) and has been re-elected three times since. He is also the President of Ethiopian Federation of Persons with Disabilities (EFPD). Since graduating from university, he has worked for the Central Statistical Authority, a government organisation.

Introduction

The Ethiopian National Association of the Deaf (ENAD) was established in 1970 by deaf people with the encouragement and help of some hearing friends. Today, the ENAD has twelve regional branch associations.

According to the 1994 Population and Housing Census (Office of the…, 1995), there are 190,220 deaf and hard of hearing people – most of them young people – in Ethiopia. In the year 2004 the estimate is expected to reach 250,000 given the 2.9 percent annual population increase per year. 87% of the population live in rural areas where there are no schools for the deaf and where there is no standardised sign language but where people use some kind of home signs to communicate with each other.

Due to the low level of deaf education, deaf people in Ethiopia, especially in rural areas, are mercilessly exposed to HIV/AIDS. Compounded with their disability, poverty and marginalization, the onslaught of HIV/AIDS threatens the extinction of the deaf community unless adequate intervention methods are taken on time.

The global and the national situation

Of the more than 40 million people who are HIV positive, 90% live in the developing world. Approximately 25.4 million HIV infected people live in Sub-Saharan Africa (UNAIDS, 2004b). In terms of the absolute numbers, Ethiopia is among the countries with the largest HIV positive populations in Africa.

HIV started to spread in Ethiopia in the early 1980s (Ethiopia Ministry of Health, 2002). The first evidence of HIV infection was found in 1984, and the first AIDS case was reported in 1986. While the HIV prevalence rate was very low in Ethiopia in the early 1980s, it has been on the rise in the past few years. By 1989, the adult HIV prevalence had increased to 2.7%. The estimated adult prevalence rate of 6.2% in 1993 increased to 7.1% in 1997 and 7.3% in 2000. The prevalence rate in 2003 in urban areas was estimated to be even higher, namely 13.4% (and 16.8% in Addis Ababa). In 2003, the total number of adults and children infected with HIV was estimated to be about 2.5 million (UNAIDS, 2004b) out of which 250,000 HIV infections are among children under the age of five years.

Figure 1: HIV Infection in Ethiopia (1980–2000)

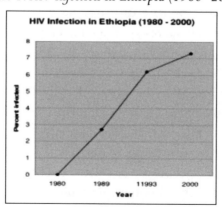

Future projections indicate that if the prevalence increases to 7.7%, the number of infected people in the population would reach three million and four million by 2006 and 2014 respectively.

Recent revisions on the statistical figures

In June 2004, the Ministry of Health issued new revised data concerning the spread of HIV/AIDS in Ethiopia. According to the new data, the number of HIV positive people was estimated to be 1.5 million. However, preliminary data issued by the World Health Organization and UNAIDS show double the figures issued by the Ethiopian government. The WHO and UNAIDS estimate that there up to three million people in Ethiopia who carry the HIVirus. Therefore, we may treat the Ethiopian government data as the lowest range of number of infected people in the country. The following table shows data provided by the Ethiopian Ministry of Health in June 2004.

Table 1: The profile of HIV/AIDS distribution in Ethiopia up to the year 2008 as a percentage of the total population

(Source: Magazine of the HIV/AIDS Prevention and Control Office, 2004)

Region	1982	1985	1990	1995	2000	2001	2002	2003	2008
National	0	0.2	1.6	3.2	3.9	4.1	4.2	4.4	5
Male	0	0.2	1.5	2.8	3.4	3.5	3.7	3.8	4.4
Female	0	0.2	1.7	3.6	4.4	4.8	4.8	5	5.7
Urban	0	0.7	7	13.4	13	12.8	12.7	12.6	12.6
Rural	0	0.1	0.3	0.8	1.9	2.1	2.4	2.6	3.4

HIV/AIDS and Deaf people in Ethiopia

So far there has been no survey on the number of deaf people infected by HIV except for some interviews made by an NGO called Handicap International in Addis Ababa in 2002. However, the number of HIV infected deaf persons is expected to be proportionally higher than that of the remaining population due to the lack of information and to misinformation. In recent years, death rates in the deaf community in Addis Ababa have been on the rise. The writer of this paper suspects that the increased untimely death rates among deaf people can be related to HIV/AIDS. Due to cultural misconceptions and marginalization, deaf people seem afraid to disclose their situation because of fears of double discrimination.

Deaf people in rural areas and small towns are highly vulnerable to HIV/AIDS due to communication problems and to their relative poverty. Hearing people think that deaf persons are free from HIV infections and tend to force or lure them for sexual abuse. Since most deaf people are poor and have not undergone any formal education they are easily exposed to various forms of abuse, including sexual harassment, which exposes them to HIV/AIDS.

The other big problem threatening deaf children is the untimely death of their parents. There are many orphaned children in Ethiopia including the deaf. There were two infant deaf children at ENAD preschool who lost their parents to AIDS. Another deaf child at the ENAD preschool last year was diagnosed HIV/AIDS positive. The child has been in the custody of another NGO and we do not know her fate. She acquired the infection from her parents. Such things are nightmarish in the deaf community.

Interventions made so far are inadequate and limited in scope. Since 2000, the ENAD has initiated and conducted some small awareness raising workshops for deaf people. However, these workshops are usually limited to Addis Ababa and to a few regional branches. In 2005, the government of Ethiopia was willing to support our activities focusing on HIV/AIDS in the larger towns. However, reaching the majority of deaf people in the rural areas is very difficult since they are scattered around the country, have no access to formal education, and often do not know sign language. In order to tackle the problem international assistance and support is necessary since the country itself is struggling with many economic and social problems.

Notes

1. An earlier version of this paper originally appeared at the March 2005 Supporting Deaf People III Online Conference, available at http://www.online-conference.net.

References

Ethiopia Ministry of Health, Disease Prevention and Control Department. (2002). *AIDS in Ethiopia* (4th ed.). Addis Ababa: Ministry of Health.

Magazine of the HIV/AIDS Prevention and Control Office, Vol. 2, No. 2. (2004, October).

Ministry of Labor and Social Affairs, UNICEF, & Italian Government. (2003). *Survey on the prevalence and characteristics of AIDS orphans in Ethiopia*.

Office of the Population and Housing Census Commission and Central Statistical Authority. (1995). *The population and housing census of Ethiopia, 1994*.

UNAIDS. (2004a). *Report on the global HIV/AIDS epidemic, July 2004*. Retrieved May 1, 2005, from http://www.unaids.org/bangkok2004/report.html

UNAIDS. (2004b). *AIDS epidemic update, December 2004*. Retrieved May 1, 2005, from http://www.unaids.org/wad2004/report.html

Contact information

Alemayehu Teferi
Ethiopian National Association of the Deaf (ENAD)
P.O. Box 21359
Addis Ababa, Ethiopia
Tel: +251 1 222517
Fax: +251 1 222516
email: enad@telecom.net.et

Brad

by Loel Poor

Deaf Worlds
2006 | vol 22 (1)
Forest Books ©
ISSN 1362–3125

I met Brad in 1997. He was deaf and living with Usher's Syndrome and AIDS. Every day, he energetically moved around New York City with his dog Odo. Occasionally, his energetic pace was punctuated by a wave of exhaustion which reminded him of the lurking virus which sapped away at his strength.

Brad first contacted me, a photographer who has worked with people living with HIV/AIDS, when he was looking for a way to advocate for other deaf people living with HIV or at heightened risk of exposure to it. His foremost concern is for deaf youth, boys mostly, who seem to have a very high risk of getting "lost in the system" out of high school. He talks at length about deaf kids who become employed in the sex industry in New York City and other cities where they sometimes can't keep up with their studies and are exploited by pimps and other hustlers. He feels certain that many of the deaf kids who are exposed to HIV haven't got a clue about the disease and the risks.

Recently, Brad was contacted by a young deaf guy whose doctor told him he was dying. The young guy couldn't understand how this was possible. "Why? When? Aren't I too young? I am deaf – why this too?" Brad took care of him until he died two weeks later as a result of his exposure to HIV.

It concerns Brad that there is still not a commonly accepted ASL sign for AIDS. He feels that deaf people are being overlooked in the education programs about AIDS.

He's right.

From the editors

The last contact Loel Poor had with Brad was in 2002 and both his health and eyesight were worsening. We are deeply saddened that efforts to contact Brad and his medical guardian by phone/TTY and mail in July 2005 failed.

This work is adapted from Poor's exhibit on Brad and others living with HIV at http://www.thebody.com/loelpoor/index.html. Photos used with her permission.

Raymond Luczak

Deaf Worlds
2006 | vol 22 (1)
Forest Books ©
ISSN 1362–3125

Biography

Raymond Luczak is the author of five books, including "Silence is a four-letter word: On art and Deafness", and a filmmaker. His full-length documentaries include: "Guy wonder: Stories and artwork" and "Nathie: No hand-me-downs". He lives in Minneapolis, MN.

Someone died today

for Robert Louis Sisco 1952–2004

Someone died today, and I feel dead and buried,
six feet deep of slight memories already decomposing
in the silt of my mind. You stand a figure in black,
eyes roving as in bar nights gone in a hourglass.
Already you are a craggy face made of sand,
crumbling into a child's castle fading in the tide.
You never shared with me words about love,
nor about those who slipped away mornings,
a time easy enough to find reasons to leave,
harder to find excuses to stay when it hurts
to see another in pain, in fear, in anger.
You never revealed why they didn't stay.

I never knew whom you'd loved, or if they
loved you back with their clumsy hands
trying to learn signs as you spoke into their ears
amidst the smoky pulse of trance music
while you fondled the thick beer bottles
you sipped from to still your loneliness. Somehow
I knew the dark valley of glances would swallow
you alive just as you would kiss a man in black,
a momentary flame of hope for a tender love
blessed with a perfect set of muscles and looks.
How you two would dance together, eyes locked
on each other, bodies on fire to conquer.

I've stopped wondering whatever will happen
to these strangers phantoming through the night,
lean shadows flickering in the strobe lights,
all filled with glances waiting for something.
But I wonder now how you explained away
your hearing aids, your hands, your loneliness
to strangers peering into your blue eyes,
windows of a strange house they'd never seen
before. Why hadn't anyone dared to call you his?
Shall I weep tonight for you whom I barely knew?
The blood inside my heart's vessel has dried out.
No words shall do when hands alone bleed.

In the pawnshop

for Alan R. Barwiolek 1952–1996

Life on the bedside table cannot be
measured. You are now a broken clock,
tossed into a box readied for pawning.
Your sentimentality is suddenly cheapened.
What would the pawnshop make of you?
No longer ticking, you have no value.

The tears of rust have streaked in the dark.
The numbers have thinned your cheeks.
Your hands of time are now ashes,
a silvery baby's powder, what time was it?
In the pawnshop you end up with the freebies.
Dust collects on your tired eyes.

In your hollow skull of broken parts,
you remember. Time was a beautiful thing.
There were so many others like you,
lined up like a toy store before a big sale.
Yet you cast a charming Swiss precision.
Everyone adored you and clamored for more.

In the pawnshop you are ignored like the rest.
Everywhere are price tags of souls gone too soon.
I cup your ashes and blow them off my palms.
They sail like comets splintering with seeds
cracking the floor in half, taking root underneath.
Though it turns, the earth is a rusted clock.

Positive feelings

An excerpt from the unpublished novel "Men With Their Hands"

Even though Stan has vowed never to get involved with another *young* man again, he can't help studying Michael's red-bearded profile. As the Deaf AIDS Project meeting progresses in the new Gay Men's Health Crisis headquarters in Chelsea, a neighborhood becoming the next hot gay area in Manhattan, Michael is looking over the group of deaf and hearing volunteers interested in helping deaf people with AIDS. Stan is quite sure from Eddie's description that Michael is the same guy he'd heard had just moved to New York. Given the deaf grapevine, it was really surprising that Stan hadn't met Michael sooner, but then it had been a long time since he went out to the bars. The year is 1985.

Stan thinks about all his deaf friends who have died. He'd never cared for hospitals, not since he was twelve and had to stay in one for three weeks with his broken leg in a cast. Yet in the last five years he'd visited at least ten of his deaf friends in hospitals. Most of them stayed at St. Vincent's Hospital, which was right in Stan's neighborhood.

He remembers moving into that tiny studio apartment on Barrow Street when he was 25 – a long time before rents all over the city shot out of sight– with only a futon, kitchen things, and clothes. Over the years the apartment had acquired its own character: how-to books, curled photographs, and a jungle of plants in its two windows. When he came home that night from cleaning out Vince's apartment after his death, he stood in the middle of his studio and thought, *Me-die next. Clean-out who?*

Two years ago he learned the results of his HIV-antibody test. He'd stopped going out to the bars when his friends began winding up in hospital beds instead; he gave up pot and Bloody Marys for brunch. He had once longed for a lover, someone exciting and vivid and perhaps as loving as Vince, but ever since the epidemic began, he knew it would no longer be possible. Who'd want a man who was positive? It did not help that he couldn't speak very clearly, either, in case some hearing man wanted him; but in any case, who knew how much time Stan had left? The clock is ticking away inside him; it torments him to think of how truly subdued and helpless Vince had become the night before he died.

Stan doesn't really need to see what his friends are saying around the table. He's seen all their arguments about how to proceed with the Deaf AIDS Project before; everyone had been given the runaround when sign language interpreters were requested for meetings with doctors.

These days he has become very close to Eddie. The irony of this hasn't escaped him: He once defended Vince when he told Eddie, "Relationships long-time sex bored easy. Relationships long-time what-for?" He wishes more than anything that he hadn't believed Vince for so long; he knows if he'd paid a little more attention to Eddie, he might've really found someone. He had decided some time ago that the size of his cramped apartment or that wanting to be "independent" were lousy excuses not to have a lover. If he had to throw out half of his things for a lover to move in, so be it. Most of his deaf gay friends here and everywhere are dead, and he is almost forty.

He watches the younger men and women chatting amiably with each other; the atmosphere feels so relaxed. It used to be that everyone *had* to cruise each other the second they arrived at some bar or a party. Michael doesn't look the type to spend weekends in bars; he doesn't carry that calculating air. He looks safe, very safe. But the problem is, he's just too *young*.

Stan strokes his moustache; he suddenly senses Michael eyeing him. He turns slowly, and now he knows they will meet up afterwards. He relaxes a little, while at the same time he poses a little. He can't help it; too many nights spent waiting in bars and bathhouses have ingrained the behavior in him. He looks at his watch now and then, and remembers the clock ticking away inside his body; he hates watches now.

Later, Michael touches him slightly on his shoulder. "Sorry not catch name yours."

As Stan almost jumps up to stand, his thighs bump the edge of the long table. "Sorry." Stan has not realized until now how intensely dark blue Michael's eyes are; they remind him of the sapphire summer skies over the Pines on Fire Island.

At the end of the night, after dinner at the cheap Greek diner just north of 14th Street, Stan walks alone to his apartment, he knows he has lost someone again, but this time there will be no memorial service. In the darkness surrounding his bed he thinks about when he was Michael's age, how he'd have given anything to be Vince's lover; and now, he wishes he had stopped Michael and explained to him how much he'd loved Vince, that he'd never really felt happy fucking one stranger after another. He'd surely understand – wouldn't he? – and look at Stan differently. But he cannot think of anything in their language close enough to describe these feelings, or even the ones he's feeling tonight.

Contact information

Raymond Luczak
P.O. Box 3941
Minneapolis, MN 55403-0941
email: RL@raymondluczak.com
http://www.raymondluczak.com

Maryland 2003 HIV infection statistics for hearing and Deaf populations: Analysis and policy suggestions

Leila Monaghan

Deaf Worlds
2006 | vol 22 (1)
Forest Books ©
ISSN 1362–3125

Keywords

HIV/AIDS, deafness, Maryland, demographics, infection rates, hearing/Deaf comparisons

Abstract

Although there is considerable speculation about the rates of HIV/AIDS infection in the Deaf population versus the hearing population, there is little information about actual rates available. This paper presents an analysis of the Maryland Department of Health and Mental Hygiene's statistics for HIV infection for the year 2003. Maryland, unlike most other states in the U.S., collects information on hearing status when collecting descriptive information from those being tested for HIV at state-run sites. In 2003, 38,602 hearing people were tested at Maryland public sites with 813 of those testing HIV positive, and 832 Deaf people were tested with 38 of those testing positive. Comparatively speaking, 2.1% of the hearing people tested were HIV+ and 4.6% of the Deaf people tested HIV+. When these figures are compared taking into account general population estimates of Deaf and hearing people in the state of Maryland, Deaf people seem to be over ten times more likely to be HIV+ than hearing people.

Although 38 cases is too small to draw definitive conclusions, the distribution of HIV infection within these cases appears to indicate that HIV infection expresses itself differently in the Deaf population than the larger hearing population. Younger Deaf people, White Deaf people and Deaf women are all more likely than their hearing counterparts to be represented in the HIV+ population. Deaf women tested, for example, are almost three times more likely (4.3% vs. 1.5%) to be positive than the hearing women in the testing sample.

Introduction

There are few good sources of information on the extent of the HIV/AIDS infection rates in Deaf communities. One hope is that this journal issue will encourage more jurisdictions to keep figures on the extent of HIV/AIDS among Deaf people, giving us a clearer idea of the overall problem. The exception to these normally sparse sources, however, are the statistics kept by the State of Maryland's Department of Health and Mental Hygiene in the United States. Presented here are Maryland's statistics for 2003[1] (the most recent year full statistics are available), giving us some idea for how the infection rates for Deaf people may be similar to or different from that of the larger population. Below are statistics from Deaf and hearing people who made use of Maryland's public confidential testing facilities (abbreviation MD 2003). These statistics show 38 Deaf people tested as HIV+ in 2003. Speaking in human terms, 38 is far too many. Statistically speaking, however, 38 is a small sample from which to determine distribution. It is also a self-selected non-random sample, so we need to understand that conclusions made about HIV infection from these numbers may change with further information. However, the direction these statistics point is sobering.

Below is an analysis of the Maryland 2003 testing data including comparisons between people who have tested positive and the general population tested, and between the Deaf population and the hearing population. These statistics begin to give us an understanding of how the incidence of HIV in the Deaf community may be similar to or different from that in the larger hearing population. The following section analyzes how these figures compare to the names of the memorial site for Deaf people who have died of AIDS and to the general population of the state of Maryland.

Analysis of the Maryland testing data

Extent of infection among people tested in Maryland in 2003

	Deaf people	Hearing people	Total
HIV+	38	813	851
All tested	832	38,602	39,434
% positive	4.6%	2.1%	

The infection rate for Deaf people who were tested in Maryland in 2003 is more than double that of the hearing people tested (117% higher). The lack of information that Goldstein, Eckhardt, Joyner and Berry (this volume) and Perlman and Leon (this volume), among others, have found seems to translate here to a higher incidence of HIV infection.

Gender

Deaf people testing HIV+[3]	n	%
Male	26	68.4%
Female	12	31.6%
Total	38	

All Deaf people tested		
Male	551	66.2%
Female	281	33.8%
Total	832	

Hearing people testing HIV+		
Male	513	63.1%
Female	300	36.9%
Total	813	

All hearing people tested		
Male	18,572	48.1%
Female	20,030	51.9%
Total	38,602	

Comparison by gender		
	Deaf people	**Hearing people**
HIV+ men	26	513
All men	551	18,572
% positive	4.7%	2.8%
HIV+ women	12	300
All women	281	20,030
% positive	4.3%	1.5%

In both the Deaf and hearing populations of the MD 2003 results, men are more likely to be HIV+ than women. In the hearing population, this difference reflects the actual distribution of being HIV+. As roughly equal numbers of men and women were tested, the different numbers of positives leads to different percentages being infected: 2.8% men versus 1.5% women are positive. The rates of infection are far closer, however, in the Deaf people that took the test: 4.7% of men and 4.3% of the women tested positive. Given that fewer women than men took the test, this implies that there are significant numbers of undiagnosed women in the population.

Age groups[2]

Deaf people testing HIV+	n	%
<20	1	2.6%
20-29	7	18.4%
30-39	9	23.7%
40-49	17	44.7%
50-59	4	10.5%
60+	0	0.0%
Total	38	

All Deaf people tested		
<20	46	5.5%
20-29	183	22.0%
30-39	223	26.8%
40-49	253	30.4%
50-59	96	11.5%
60+	31	3.7%
Total	832	

Hearing people testing HIV+		
<20	32	3.9%
20-29	130	16.0%
30-39	297	36.5%
40-49	286	35.2%
50-59	60	7.4%
60+	8	1.0%
Total	813	

All hearing people tested		
<20	6,676	17.3%
20-29	14,931	38.7%
30-39	9,011	23.3%
40-49	6,059	15.7%
50-59	1,595	4.1%
60+	330	0.9%
Total	38,602	

Comparison of age brackets	Deaf people	Hearing people
<20 HIV+	1	32
All <20	46	6,672
% positive	2.2%	0.5%
20-29 HIV+	7	130
All 20-29	183	14,931
% positive	3.8%	0.9%
30-39 HIV+	9	297
All 30-39	183	9,011
% positive	4.9%	3.3%
40-49 HIV+	17	286
All 40-49	253	6,059
% positive	6.7%	4.7%
50-59 HIV+	4	60
All 50-59	96	1,595
% positive	4.2%	3.8%
60+ HIV+	0	8
All 60+	31	330
% positive	0.0%	2.4%

The small numbers we are dealing with here (for example, where one person can represent 2.6% of the sample) means we must be extremely careful about generalizing, but the trends are clear. For every age category but the one for people 60+, Deaf people have a greater risk of infection (a ratio of >1) than their hearing counterparts. The younger the Deaf person, the proportionally greater their risk will be to be HIV+ than their hearing counterparts. This indicates that although the problem of HIV infection among younger Deaf people is not as serious as among older groups, compared to the infection rates of their hearing counterparts, younger Deaf people seem much more at risk than their hearing counterparts.

Chart 1: Ratio of Deaf to hearing infection rates

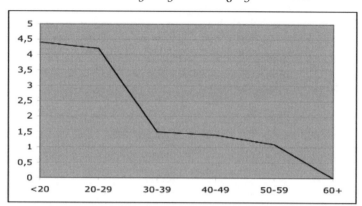

Ethnicity

Deaf people testing HIV+	n	%
White	6	15.8%
African American	31	81.6%
Hispanic[4]	1	2.6%
Other[5]	0	0.0%
Total	38	

All Deaf people tested		
White	322	38.7%
African American	487	58.5%
Hispanic	15	1.8%
Other	8	1.0%
Total	832	

Hearing people testing HIV+

White	59	7.3%
African American	740	91.0%
Hispanic	5	0.6%
Other	5	0.6%
Total	813	

All hearing people tested

White	14,499	37.6%
African American	21,731	56.3%
Hispanic	1,800	4.7%
Other	572	1.5%
Total	38,602	

Comparison of different ethnic groups

	Deaf people	Hearing people
White HIV+	6	59
All White	322	14,499
% Positive	1.9%	0.4%
African American HIV+	31	740
All African American	487	21,731
% Positive	6.4%	3.4%
Hispanic HIV+	1	5
All Hispanic	15	1,800
% Positive	0.7%	0.3%
Other HIV+	0	5
All HIV	8	572
% Positive	0.0%	0.9%

Similar proportions of White and African American people hearing and Deaf people were tested, but the extent of HIV is different between these groups. Among the hearing people tested, 91.0% of the people testing positive are African American, 7.3% were White, and .6% were Hispanic. Again, we have to be careful because of the small numbers involved but there are some interesting differences. Among Deaf people tested, 81.6% of people testing positive are African American, 15.8% are White and 2.6% are Hispanic. The problem among African American Deaf people is severe but there is also an important problem in the White and perhaps the Hispanic populations. As was shown with the breakdown among women and young people, just because the problem of HIV/AIDS might be less in a group in hearing society, it does not mean that HIV is not still an issue in the equivalent Deaf group.

Suspected mode of exposure[6]

Deaf people testing HIV+	n	%
MSM IDU[7]	0	0.0%
MSM[8]	3	7.9%
Hetsex IDU[9]	19	50.0%
Sex partner at risk	16	42.1%
Sex for drugs/money	0	0.0%
Sex w/ non-inj drugs[10]	0	0.0%
Victim of sex assault	0	0.0%
Other[11]	0	0.0%
Not specified/missing	0	——
Total	38	

All Deaf people tested		
MSM IDU	7	0.9%
MSM	36	4.4%
Hetsex IDU	190	23.1%
Sex partner at risk	521	63.3%
Sex for drugs/money	2	0.2%
Sex w/ non-inj drugs	15	1.8%
Victim of sex assault	0	0.0%
Other	61	7.4%
Not specified/missing	9	——
Total	832	

Hearing people testing HIV+		
MSM IDU	28	3.8%
MSM	92	12.5%
Hetsex IDU	256	34.7%
Sex partner at risk	260	35.2%
Sex for drugs/money	5	0.7%
Sex while using non-inj drugs	11	1.5%
Victim of sexual assault	2	0.3%
Other	84	11.4%
Not specified/missing	75	——
Total	813	

All hearing people tested		
MSM IDU	810	2.2%
MSM	983	2.7%
Hetsex IDU	4,502	12.3%
Sex partner at risk	23,740	64.7%
Sex for drugs/money	531	0.3%
Sex while using non-inj drugs	134	1.4%
Victim of sexual assault	2	0.4%
Other	5,906	16.1%
Not specified/missing	1,888	——
Total	38,602	

Comparison of types of exposure		
	Deaf people	**Hearing people**
MSM IDU HIV+	0	28
All MSM IDU	7	810
% Positive	0.0%	3.5%
MSM HIV+	3	92
All MSM	36	983
% Positive	8.3%	9.4%
Hetsex IDU HIV+	19	256
All Hetsex IDU	190	4,502
% Positive	10.0%	5.7%
Sex partner at risk HIV+	16	260
All sex partner at risk	521	23,740
% Positive	3.1%	1.1%

Sex for drugs/money HIV+	0	5
All Sex for drugs/money	2	108
% Positive	0.0%	4.6%
Sex w/ non-inj drugs HIV+	0	11
All Sex w/ non-inj drugs	15	531
% Positive	0.0%	2.1%
Victim of Sex Assault HIV+	0	2
All Victim of Sex Assault	0	134
% Positive	0.0%	1.5%
Other HIV+	0	84
All Other	61	5,906
% Positive	0.0%	1.4%

This category is the most problematic to analyze because the suspected cause of transmission is far more likely to be left blank than factors such as gender or age. The most severe problem for Deaf people is among intravenous drug users. One in every ten Deaf IDUs tested HIV+, almost double that in the hearing population of IDUs. Also an issue is transmission by males having sex with males, although the rate among Deaf people is slightly lower than among hearing people (though the sample is so small that a 1% difference is not particularly meaningful).

Intravenous drug users are particularly at risk and represent 23.1% of Deaf people tested. HIV infection among IDUs is particularly problematic since HIV can be spread in this population in multiple ways including sharing drug paraphernalia and sexual contact. According to Liitsola et al., "Epidemics amongst IDU have in the past been characterized frequently by the rapid spread of the virus in the IDU population and subsequent spread to other population groups" (1998, p. 1908).[12] Given these problems, more people should be tested. There are also members of other at risk categories such as those who have sex for drugs or money and victims of sexual assault that might well have been exposed to HIV but who have not been tested. More information should be available to members of all risk categories on the benefits of testing.

Place of testing

Deaf people testing HIV+	n	%
Baltimore city & county	20	52.6%
Washington D.C. suburbs[13]	3	7.9%
Corrections[14]	15	39.5%
Juvenile justice	0	0.0%
Other counties	0	0.0%
Missing	0	——
Total	38	

All Deaf people tested		
Baltimore city & county	309	37.2%
Washington D.C. suburbs	69	8.3%
Corrections	248	29.9%
Juvenile justice	0	0.0%
Other counties	204	24.6%
Missing	2	——
Total	832	

Hearing people testing HIV+		
Baltimore city & county	523	64.3%
Washington D.C. suburbs	80	9.8%
Corrections	163	20.0%
Juvenile justice	0	0.0%
Other counties	47	5.8%
Missing	0	——
Total	813	

All hearing people tested		
Baltimore city & county	11,731	30.4%
Washington D.C. suburbs	7,386	19.1%
Corrections	5,102	13.3%
Juvenile justice	30	0.1%
Other counties	14,339	37.2%
Missing	21	——
Total	38,602	

Comparison of results from locations	Deaf people	Hearing people
Baltimore HIV+	20	523
All Baltimore	309	11,731
% Positive	6.5%	4.5%
Washington D.C. suburbs HIV+	3	80
All Washington D.C. suburbs	69	7,386
% Positive	4.3%	1.1%
Corrections/JJ HIV+	15	163
All corrections/JJ	248	5,132
% Positive	6.0%	3.2%
Other counties HIV+	0	47
All other counties	47	14,339
% Positive	0.0%	0.3%

Once again, in these MD 2003 results Deaf people appear more likely to be HIV+ than their hearing counterparts. Deaf people in the Baltimore data are almost 50% more likely to be positive than their hearing neighbors, the small (and therefore unreliable) number in the D.C. suburbs indicates that Deaf people have approximately four times the chance of being positive than hearing people from the area, and incarcerated Deaf people are almost twice as likely to be positive as their hearing counterparts. The concentration of HIV cases in these urban areas and in the incarcerated population point to the need for good services, sign language accessible counseling and education at these sites. The high percentage of cases diagnosed in corrections settings shows the vital nature of testing in such situations and the need to have deafness recognized as one risk factor for HIV infection. Despite the significantly greater proportion of young Deaf people being infected, no young Deaf people were tested in the Juvenile Justice system in 2003.

Relatively few Deaf people from other, more suburban and rural counties, were tested and none were found to be positive. As the general rate in the population is low, however, it is hard to conclude that Deaf people are safe from HIV/AIDS in even these non-urban settings. There should also be outreach to make sure that there are not undiagnosed cases in these areas.

Alternate ways of judging the HIV/AIDS epidemic

This paper is just a quantitative presentation of these results from Maryland's public testing sites to make them available to a larger audience. Much more qualitative and quantitative work needs to be done to understand the extent and causes of this AIDS epidemic in the Deaf community in the U.S. and elsewhere. In this section, I present three very rough alternate ways of estimating the extent of the HIV/AIDS problem including estimating from a public listing of Deaf people who have died from AIDS and by estimating from two different and rather crude Maryland Deaf population statistics.

The *Remember Their Names* memorial site

The *Remember Their Names* website lists 343 Deaf people from the United States among the people in the Deaf community who have died of HIV/AIDS (Deaf HIV/AIDS Resources, 2006). If we estimate, as a similar site for Washington, D.C. area AIDS deaths does (Rainbow History Project, 2006), that the people listed represent only 30% of the actual number of deaths, we would get a figure of approximately 1,100 deaths in the U.S. Deaf community from AIDS. This translates to a rate approximately 25% higher than the deaths in the general U.S. population.[15] Not as high a rate as the Maryland figures suggest but still serious. Given the lack of computer and literacy skills of some members of the community, this list might be even more of an undercount than the D.C. site, pointing back towards the almost 100% higher numbers of the Maryland figures.

What the *Remember Their Names* (RTN) site offers that the Maryland numbers do not is specific names and thus gives a small sense of the reach of the epidemic. Both the prominent and the humble have been affected. One person listed is the late actor, author and activist Bruce Hlibok (see Bryan, 2002), the opposite end of the social spectrum to the young men described by the HIV activist Brad as "lost in the system," and as "the deaf kids who are exposed to HIV [that] haven't got a clue about the disease and the risks" (Poor, this volume).

The names can also give a very rough sense of the gender and ethnic break down of these reported deaths. Although it is hard to definitively ascertain either sex or ethnicity from only name information, the names could be sorted by traditional gender and ethnic naming patterns.[16] General U.S. figures from 2000 are also presented for the sake of comparison.

Remember Their Names entries of deaths by gender (January, 2006)

Gender	Number	Percentage
Male	322	94%
Female	12	3%
Unknown	9	3%
Total	343	100%

Death due to AIDS by gender (Whitehouse, 2006; figures from 2000)

Male	85%
Female	15%

The general U.S. rate of 85% deaths being male is explained in part by how it was at first spread rapidly through communities of men having sex with men (MSM). This gender split is even more pronounced in the RTN information, where at least 94% of the entries are male. This is very different from the 2003 Maryland testing data of 68% male and 32% female and perhaps reflects the willingness of the Deaf male Gay community to report deaths by AIDS rather than lack of deaths of female AIDS patients. As Raymond Luczak's short story (this volume) reflects, the problem of HIV/AIDS has been well known in the Deaf Gay community for many years. While continuing attention needs to be paid to safe sex behaviors for all people, given the disparity between the testing results and the publicly announced deaths, more attention in particular should be paid to informing Deaf women of the problem of HIV/AIDS and dealing with issues of stigma in the community.

Remember Their Names entries of deaths by ethnicity (January, 2006)

Ethnicity	Number	Percentage
Anglo or African American	200	58%
African American	16	5%
White Ethnic	85	25%
Latino	35	10%
Asian American	1	<1%
Asian International	4	1%
International Unknown	2	1%
Total	343	100%

Death due to AIDS by race/ethnicity (Whitehouse, 2006; figures from 2000)

Ethnicity	Deaths	U.S. population
White, non-Hispanic	46%	71%
African American	35%	12%
Latino	17%	13%
Asian/Pacific Islander	1%	4%
American Indian/Alaska Native	<1%	1%

It is hard to judge the balance of African Americans and Anglo Americans from the names of the deceased at the RTN site. More research on the background and histories of the deceased needs to be done but this is beyond the scope of this article. What can be noted is that the distribution of HIV infection for these reported deaths is different from that of the 2003 Maryland cases. While only 16% of the Deaf cases and 7% of the hearing cases in Maryland are White, at least 25%, if not considerably more, of the RTN reported deaths are White. There are also more Latino deaths reported in the RTN statistics than in the Maryland figures. One Deaf Latino person tested HIV+ in Maryland (2.6% of this small sample) while 35 Latino people (10%) were listed as having died from AIDS in the RTN list. The RTN results reflect nationwide deaths and are halfway between the general national rate of 17% of AIDS deaths being Latino (Whitehouse, 2006) and the MD 2003 statistics for Deaf HIV+ people.

One can see at least three factors contributing to the differences between the Maryland and these national RTN figures. First, who has been most affected by AIDS over the years has changed. Second, more White people have easy access to computers so are more likely to report the deaths of friends and family. Finally, the split between Maryland and national statistics points to the geographic distribution of the AIDS epidemic in the United States. The higher overall rate for Latinos in the RTN list reflects the presence of AIDS in areas such as New York, California, Florida, Texas and Puerto Rico which all have significant Latino populations (Kaiser, 2005, p. 1).

Top 10 states/areas AIDS case rate (2003):
General cumulative reported AIDS cases (1981–2003)*

New York	162,446
California	133,292
Florida	94,725
Texas	62,983
New Jersey	46,703
Illinois	30,139
Pennsylvania	29,988
Puerto Rico	28,301
Georgia	27,915
Maryland	26,918
Subtotal	643,410
U.S. total	902,223

Top 10 states/areas: General AIDS case rate per 100,000 population (2003)*

District of Columbia	170.6
New York	34.8
Virgin Islands	31.2
Maryland	28.5
Puerto Rico	27.5
Florida	27.4
Delaware	26.1
Louisiana	23.2
Georgia	22.0
Connecticut	21.1

*Charts adapted from Kaiser (2005, p.1)

This second chart shows Washington, D.C. as the epicenter of the U.S. AIDS crisis. Maryland, adjacent to D.C., had the fourth highest rate per 100,000 in the nation in 2003. Unfortunately for Deaf people, Washington D.C. is also the center of U.S. Deaf culture including the home of Gallaudet University.

Two estimates of the extent of HIV/AIDS based upon estimates of the Maryland Deaf population

According to July 1, 2003 U.S. Census Bureau estimates, Maryland had a population of 5,508,909 people (U.S. Census Bureau, 2004) and according to MD 2003, 39,434 of these people had themselves tested for HIV/AIDS, 0.72% of the population, and 851 were found to be HIV+. This means that 0.015% of the general population (hearing and Deaf) of Maryland were diagnosed as HIV+ in 2003 at the state testing sites. The crude estimate of the population over 16 "who can't hear normal conversation" in Maryland was 17,089 (Harrington, 2004). If the number is adjusted to add the approximately 24% of the population that is 16 and under,[17] we get roughly 22,600 people. Using these adjusted figures, we get 3.7% of the Deaf population being tested (832 people), and 0.17% testing HIV+ (38 people). When compared to the MD 2003 hearing people tested, this gives us the very sobering figures of Deaf people in the testing results being 5.1 times more likely to be tested and 10.9 more likely to be HIV+.

Problems here include the general unreliability of the estimate and that the definition of deafness is not clear. Tom Harrington, the Gallaudet research librarian who prepared these statistics based on U.S. census figures, clearly warns that the numbers are estimates. "When using this data, it must be remembered that it is *not* based on any actual counting of Deaf people, and could be different from reality" (Harrington, 2004, p. 1). The numbers are also based on 1994 census documents that have not yet been updated.

Given the age of these statistics, it is useful to also estimate the Deaf population of Maryland based on national estimates. A recent rough estimate of people self-identifying as Deaf in the United States is 500,000 (Mitchell, Young, Bachleda & Karchmer, 2005). Given a general U.S. population of 295,734,134 (CIA, 2005) the percentage of Deaf people in the U.S. can be estimated to be 0.17%. If the proportion of people who are Deaf in

Maryland were the same as the proportion of Deaf people in the whole country, there would be approximately 9,315 Deaf people in Maryland. Using this figure, we get the proportions of 12.5 as many Deaf people testing themselves and a staggering 26.4 times as many Deaf as hearing people testing HIV+ in the MD 2003 figures. Given that Maryland is a center for Deaf people in the United States, this is likely to an over-estimate but it does support the higher figures of the estimates based on the Harrington calculations above.

Summary of findings on HIV status

Data type	Findings	Calculation of effect
Deaf U.S. deaths as reported on *Remember Their Names* website	estimated 1,100 deaths	1.25 times greater than U.S. hearing population
Percentage of HIV+ as reported by MD 2003 testing figures, Deaf testers vs. hearing testers	4.6% of Deaf testers HIV+	2.2 times greater than MD hearing population
Percentage of HIV+ MD 2003 adjusted for Harrington population estimates	0.17% of total MD 2003 Deaf population tested HIV+	10.9 times greater than MD hearing population
Percentage of HIV+ MD 2003 adjusted for Mitchell et al. population estimate	0.41% of total MD 2003 Deaf population tested HIV+	26.4 times greater than MD hearing population

Discussion

According to the 2003 data, the nature of the HIV/AIDS epidemic among Deaf people is probably different and more severe than that in the hearing population. The Deaf people tested in Maryland public facilities were twice as likely to be infected as the hearing people tested. Although it is difficult to judge because of the inaccuracy of the population statistics for Deaf people, estimates of Deaf people being ten times more likely to be HIV+ point to an epidemic that threatens not only the lives of Deaf people but larger hearing populations as well. The public health issues of Deaf people are inextricably entwined with the public health of entire nations.

While the distribution of HIV infection in the Maryland Deaf population mirrors that of the larger hearing population, there are important variations in the distribution of infection. Deaf men, Deaf African American people, and Deaf people over the age of 30 tested in 2003 were one and a half to two times more likely to be infected than the hearing people tested. Deaf women, Deaf White people, and Deaf people under the age of 30 were three to five times more likely to be infected than their hearing counterparts who were tested. These rates also do not take into account the perhaps fivefold multiplying factors that the adjustment for population distributions calls for. Estimates for the prevalence of HIV/AIDS in specific sub-populations of the Deaf community compared to the larger general population are not given here because of the difficulties of estimation from such a small group of cases and such poor demographic information on the Deaf population of the United States but would be extremely useful if done with more extensive data than can be presented here. From my own experiences with the Maryland Deaf community I think that the Deaf population of the state is significantly higher than the 0.17% average nationwide figure that generated the figure that Deaf people are 26.4 times more likely to be infected than hearing people in the state, making this number unreliable. This 26.4 times estimate, however, does add plausibility to the 10.9 times estimate based on the adapted 1994 census figures.

Other articles in this volume suggest some of the reasons that HIV/AIDS is such a problem in Deaf communities including lack of information and services accessible in sign language. Surveys done by Goldstein et al. (this volume) and Perlman and Leon (this volume) show that Deaf people often do not have the information about HIV/AIDS that they need to prevent infection. Deaf social networks are also close knit and can be sexually active so one person who is unaware of his or her HIV status can impact a wide range of people. The lack of economic resources in the Deaf communities also compounds the problem. Another contributing factor to the American Deaf HIV/AIDS epidemic is that Washington D.C. and nearby Maryland are epicenters of the epidemic as well as centers for the Deaf community nationally. Of particular concern is that the largest city in Maryland,

Baltimore, is also the leading center for heroin use in the United States (Craig, 2000). Among the 38 Deaf people testing HIV+, 50% were intravenous drug users. Given that IDUs, as has been shown in a number of European cities, can be flashpoints for the start of much larger epidemics, this creates the possibility for an epidemic even more serious than the one that has been documented here.

The deaths recorded by the *Remember Their Names* website (Deaf HIV/AIDS resources, 2006) show that the incidence of HIV/AIDS in the United States is different from that reported in the Maryland 2003 figures. This is both because the nationwide nature of the epidemic has changed over time, moving from a disease that predominantly affected White Gay men (including White Gay Deaf men) to one that affected communities of color, and because the demographics of Maryland are different from those of other states like New York, Florida and California. Deaths are not listed by date but do reflect the past rather than the present nature of the epidemic. The origins of the epidemic as one of Gay men is reflected in the high percentages of men listed on the website while the difference between the demographics of Maryland and the nation as a whole demographics is particularly evident in the number of Latino names. While the estimate of the HIV/AIDS epidemic in the Deaf population being 26.4 times that of the hearing population is probably too high, the conservative estimate of the epidemic based on extrapolation from these names being 1.25 times that of the hearing community is probably considerably too low. The 10.9 figure is also based on fuzzy population estimates but is probably closer to the right number. My best guess is that the correct figure is higher than the 2.2 times of the MD 2003 numbers but a bit less than the 10.9 adjusted for general population.

One troubling implication of the undercount of AIDS deaths on the *Remember Their Names* site is that this might be so because many Deaf people are out of the computer literate social networks that might post such names and thus cut off from social networks with good access to information and resources to deal with the epidemic as well. As in the larger society, the poor and disenfranchised are at particular risk. These risks are multiply compounded when accessible information, counseling and treatment options are not available.

Policy suggestions

Education efforts that are working to reduce the incidence rate of HIV in hearing populations must be adapted for the Deaf population and must reflect the different nature of the extent of the disease. One area for particular focus should be the intravenous drug using populations of Baltimore and Washington D.C., stigmatized groups that seem to be unusually vulnerable to infection.

Testing, counseling and treatment including anti-retroviral therapies must be made easily accessible, including help from trained Deaf counselors fluent in sign language. The extent of infection in this study implies that there are many others out there that need to be reached. Services for incarcerated Deaf people and their families are particularly important given the rates of infection in corrections facilities.

More research is needed on this topic. This small analysis suggests that there may be important differences between Deaf and hearing populations. Long term quantitative work, similar data collection in other localities and qualitative ethnographic work would all shed invaluable light on these vital issues. This volume is only a start at collecting different kinds of information on the dimensions of the problem of HIV/AIDS among Deaf people. Much more work needs to be done.

To my knowledge, only the state of Maryland keeps HIV testing statistics according to hearing status. Given the severe problem that HIV/AIDS presents for Deaf communities world wide, local and national public health institutions should keep statistics on hearing status of everyone who tests HIV+, is living with HIV/AIDS, or who has died of AIDS.

Additional work is also needed on Deaf demographics in general. The reason there are such dramatically different estimates as 10.9 and 26.4 times the Deaf population being infected as the hearing population is because there is no actual enumeration of the Deaf population of Maryland, the United States or most other local governments or nations. The 2000 census collected only information about disabilities in general. These statistics are of little help when trying to understand the patterns of Deaf communities, including the patterns of HIV/AIDS infections.

All people must work to counter the stigma of HIV/AIDS at large and in the Deaf community in particular. One small way that can help is honoring those who have died by posting their names on the *Remember Their Names* website.

Notes

1. Many thanks to the Maryland Department of Health and Mental Hygiene (MDHMH) for providing the statistics from Maryland's public testing sites. The author's contribution in regards to these figures is only their analysis and she is indebted to the MDHMH for the original collection of these statistics. Many thanks also to Marjory Goldstein for pointing the way to these statistics.

2. Age in years at the time of testing in 2003.

3. This table and others may not add up to 100% because of errors introduced by rounding errors.

4. "Hispanic" is the term used on the Maryland forms for people identifying themselves as of Latino or Hispanic origin.

5. The category "Other" includes people of Asian, Native American descent and those who formally marked "Other" or multiple races on their information forms.

6. The category "Missing" is not included in the total percentages.

7. MSM IDU: Males who have had sex with males who are also intravenous drug users.

8. MSM: Males who have had sex with other males.

9. Hetsex IDU: Heterosexual intravenous drug users.

10. Sex w/ non-inj drugs: Sexual activity while under the influence of non-intravenous drugs.

11. Other: includes child of woman w/ HIV/AIDS, STD diagnosis, hemophilia/transfusion, health care exposure, and other. These were collapsed into one category because they were not reflected in Maryland's Deaf HIV+ population. This does not mean these forms are not important forms of transmission elsewhere or that they might not be present in another year's testing results.

12. For example, the HIV/AIDS epidemic currently sweeping Eastern Europe is being spread along with heroin from Afghanistan (Gosline, 2005).

13. Washington D.C. suburbs are defined here as Montgomery and Prince Georges counties, the Maryland counties directly adjacent to Washington D.C. Since this study was done in Maryland only, it does not reflect any testing done in Washington D.C. or the D.C. Virginia suburbs.

14. "Corrections" is testing done in the jails and prisons of Maryland by the Maryland Department of Health and Mental Hygiene.

15. This number is calculated from an estimation of Deaf U.S. deaths from HIV/AIDS, (343 [Deaf HIV/AIDS resources, 2005] * 3.3 [estimate of undercounting from Rainbow History Project, 2004)] divided by general Deaf population (500,000 [Mitchell, et al., 2005]) all divided by the general U.S. projection of deaths (529,113 [Avert.org, 2004 from CDC, 2004] divided by the general U.S. population (295,734,134 [CIA, 2005]). (1131.9/500,000=.00226, 529,113/295,734,134 = .001789, .00226/.001789= 1.263, thus the Deaf rate from this very rough estimate is 126% of the general rate, approximately 25% greater.)

16. For example, the listing of the late Beatrice Smith was counted as female in these calculations while the listing of Eddie Smith was counted as male. One problematic aspect ascertaining gender by name of this is that the Rainbow History Project's (2006) listing of AIDS deaths in Washington D.C. includes a number of people listed with both male and female names, presumably from the cross-dressing or transvestite communities of the city. Such a person would only be listed with one name on the Deaf *Remember Their Names* site. For ethnic naming patterns, categories were Anglo- or African American names (for example Kenneth Miller), African American names (e.g. Wendol Miller), White ethnic names (e.g. Richard Blumenfeld), Latino names (e.g. Hector Rosario), Asian American (e.g. Alex Chung), International Asian (e.g. Lam Ying), and International of Unknown background (e.g. Khae Saeteun).

17. This 24% derives from the "Total population by age, race and Hispanic or Latino origin for the United States: 2000" table (U.S. Census Bureau, 2001), and calculated by dividing the sum of all categories for children 14 and under and 2/5's (40%) of the category 15–19 by the 2000 U.S. population. My assumption is that the relationship between categories is more stable than the specific numbers of any category.

References

Bryan, A. M. "Jade". (2002). On and off stage: The Bruce Hlibok story. New York: DeafVision Filmworks. (video and DVD).

CIA. (2005). *The world factbook: Rank order – population*. Retrieved February 5, 2006, from http://www.cia.gov/cia/publications/factbook/rankorder/2119rank.html

Craig, T. (2000, July 29). Drugs worsen in city, U.S. says: Traffic in cocaine, heroin, Ecstasy assessed by DEA. *Baltimore Sun*. Retrieved February 5, 2006, from http://www.geocities.com/grantorino.geo/heroin072900.htm

Deaf HIV/AIDS resources. (2006). *Remember their names*. Retrieved February 5, 2006, from http://www.deafaids.info/remember/their_names.html

Goldstein, M. F., Eckhardt, E., Joyner, P., & Berry, R. (this volume). An HIV knowledge and attitude survey of Deaf U.S. adults.

Gosline, A. (2005, July 26). HIV epidemic sweeps along the heroin highways. *NewScientist.com news service, 17:18*. Retrieved February 5, 2006, from http://www.newscientist.com/article.ns?id=dn7732

Harrington, T. (2004). *Statistics: Deaf population of the United States*. Gallaudet University Library Deaf-related resources, frequently asked questions. Retrieved February 5, 2006, from http://library.gallaudet.edu/dr/faq-statistics-deaf-us.htm

Kaiser. (2005). *HIV/AIDS policy fact sheet: The HIV/AIDS epidemic in the United States, September 2005*. Retrieved February 5, 2006, from http://www.kff.org/ content/factsheets.cfm?topic=hivaids

Liitsola, K., Tashkinova, I., Laukkanen, T., Korovina, G., Smolskaja, T., Momot, O., Mashkilleyson, N., Chaplinskas, S., Brummer-Korvenkontio, H., Vanhatalo, J., Leinikki, P., & Salminen, M. O. (1998). HIV-1 genetic subtype A/B recombinant strain causing an explosive epidemic in injecting drug users in Kaliningrad. *AIDS, 12(14)*, 1907–1919.

Luczak, R. (this volume). Positive feelings.

Mitchell, R. E., Young, T. A., Bachleda, B., & Karchmer, M. A. (2005). *How many people use ASL in the United States? Why estimates need updating.* Gallaudet Research Institute, Gallaudet University, Washington, D.C. February 15, 2005.

Perlman, T. S., & Leon, S. C. (this volume). Preventing AIDS in the Midwest: The design and efficacy of culturally sensitive HIV/AIDS prevention education materials for Deaf communities.

Poor, B. (this volume). Brad.

Rainbow History Project. (2006). *Heroes: Rembering those we lost to AIDS.* Retrieved February 5, 2006, from http://www.rainbowhistory.org/chronAIDSlosses.pdf

U.S. Census Bureau. (2001). *Population by age, sex, race, and Hispanic or Latino origin for the United States: 2000 (PHC-T-9).* Internet Release Date: October 3, 2001.

U.S. Census Bureau, Population Division. (2004). *Annual estimates of the population for the counties of Maryland: April 1, 2000 to July 1, 2003 (CO-EST2003-01-24).* Release date: April 9, 2004.

Whitehouse. (2006). *The HIV/AIDS epidemic: 20 years in the U.S.* Retrieved February 5, 2006, from http://www.whitehouse.gov/onap/facts.html

Sexuality and HIV/AIDS education among Deaf and hard of hearing students

Gwendolyn S. Roberts

Deaf Worlds
2006 | vol 22 (1)
Forest Books ©
ISSN 1362–3125

Key words

HIV/AIDS, Deaf/Hard of Hearing, sexuality/sexual health, adolescents/youth/young adults, students, school/college/university.

Abstract

Deaf and hard of hearing adolescents and young adults are at an increased risk of HIV/AIDS in comparison to their hearing peers. Current sexuality and HIV/AIDS education initiatives among Deaf and hard of hearing students are discussed, though not a great deal of previous, recent literature is available for review. Knowledge of HIV/AIDS tends to be lower among Deaf and hard of hearing youth due to challenges in communication of sexual health education. Cultural and language barriers for Deaf and hard of hearing youth are often found among their families and educational institutions. Appropriate teaching methods incorporating visual learning are not integrated into curricula to accommodate Deaf and hard of hearing students. Most often, Deaf and hard of hearing students receive their sexuality and HIV/AIDS education from their peers, which is frequently a highly inaccurate source of information.

Trained Deaf peer health educators, however, can offer an effective way to impart information. Gallaudet University, the university for Deaf individuals in Washington D.C., through its Health and Wellness Programs (HWP) successfully provides sexuality and HIV/AIDS education to Deaf and hard of hearing college students by way of Peer Health Advocates (PHAs). The PHAs are extensively trained to become knowledgeable and skilled role-models who provide accurate sexuality and HIV/AIDS information for other students on campus. PHAs formally and informally teach sexuality and HIV/AIDS information to the Gallaudet University campus community on the individual, group, and community levels. Outreach is conducted by the PHAs in a variety of visual approaches, from presentations and workshops to skits and special events to flyers and banners. HWP has many innovative ideas and collaborative connections to implement in the near future on Gallaudet University's campus to educate Deaf and hard of hearing students about valuable sexuality and HIV/AIDS information.

Biography

Gwendolyn Suzanne Roberts is the Health and Wellness Programs Coordinator at Gallaudet University in Washington, D.C. She is also currently in the Public and Community Health doctoral program at the University of Maryland. Her dissertation will focus on communication issues of sexuality information among Deaf and hard of hearing college students. Previously, Roberts directed the Wellness and Fitness Programs and was a faculty member in the Exercise Science Department at The George Washington University in Washington, D.C. Prior to her employment, Roberts received her Master's of Public Health with an emphasis in Health Promotion and Disease Prevention at The George Washington University. During her studies at The George Washington University, she was instrumental in leading the Student Health Services sexuality peer health education program. While at the University of Maryland Baltimore County for her undergraduate studies in Sociology with an emphasis in Women's Health, Roberts, herself, was a sexuality peer health educator.

Introduction

Adolescents and young adults often feel invincible in regards to HIV infection (Luckner & Gonzales, 1993). Svenson, Carmel and Varnhagen (1997) found that 90% of college students in the United States do not recognize the likelihood of contracting HIV/AIDS themselves. HIV status may be unknown to many youth due to the latency period, so the negative health consequences for the individual may not become apparent until s/he has already infected others. Previous studies show that risky sexual activity in adolescents has been on the rise for the past decade. In the general U.S. adolescent population, the first sexual intercourse experience is occurring at a younger age, there is an increase in the reported number of sexual partners, and reported condom use is low (Svenson et al., 1997). In the 2003 U.S. Centers for Disease Control and Prevention (CDC) Youth Risk Behavior Surveillance report, 47% of high school students had ever had sexual intercourse, 14% had four or more sex partners, 34% had sexual intercourse during the past three months, and 37% of sexually active students did not use a condom during the last sexual intercourse (CDC, 2004a).

Deaf youth in the United States have been found to possess the same sense of invincibility as hearing adolescents, which increases their risk of HIV infection (Friess, 1998). The findings of the Peer Health Advocates (PHAs) at Gallaudet University for Deaf individuals in Washington, D.C., show that Gallaudet's students share many of these feelings of invincibility and how they often lack solid information about sexuality and HIV/AIDS. The PHAs have found over the years that Deaf and hard of hearing college students tend to misperceive the severity of the outcomes of risky sexual behaviors. Students do not recognize the negative consequences from decisions they make regarding sexual practices, or may not even be aware of all of the possible results that may occur due to their actions. During many of the presentations on campus, the PHAs are shocked about the myths that are believed to be true and by how little accurate sexuality information Gallaudet University college students have overall. One female student had had a child previously, and she was still unsure of her own reproductive anatomy. Some females do not seem to have the sexual education knowledge to know that they can say no to sexual intercourse with their boyfriends because many feel that sexual intercourse is expected in a relationship, although condoms and other contraception is not often used.

The most recent statistics available from the CDC indicate 37,599 HIV cases have been diagnosed among adolescents and young adults, including 1,991 new cases in 2003 (CDC, 2004b). Primarily due to risky sexual behaviors, AIDS was the fifth leading cause of death among 15–24-year-olds in the United States in 1999 (CDC, 2002). According to the National Center for Health Statistics (NCHS), there are approximately 20 million Deaf and hard of hearing individuals in the United States. The NCHS classifies Deafness and hearing trouble by various levels and types of hearing loss, capacity to hear and understand speech, early or later age at onset of hearing loss, the use of hearing aids, causes of hearing loss, and frequency of ringing in the ears (Ries, 1994). Friess (1998), Gaskins (1999), and Determan, Kordus and DeCarlo (1999) can only estimate that 7,000 to 26,000 Deaf individuals in the United States have been infected with HIV because the CDC does not report statistics specifically for Deaf individuals, as they do for other subpopulations. Figures are not available for Washington, D.C., but figures from 2003 for nearby Maryland show that 4.6% of Deaf people tested for HIV have been found to be positive in comparison to 2.1% of the hearing people tested. Within the less-than-20-year-old age group, 2.2% of Deaf people versus 0.5% of hearing people tested HIV positive, and in the 20–29 year old age group 3.5% of Deaf versus 0.9% of hearing people were reported to be HIV positive (Monaghan, this volume). These figures also do not take into consideration overall population rates which could be much higher.

As Luckner and Gonzales argue, Deaf adolescents have "important gaps in their knowledge of how HIV and AIDS are transmitted and prevented, and who can get AIDS" (1993, p. 338). This knowledge gap is reflected in all the work on Deafness, AIDS and young people. Work on sexuality in the 1980s (Fitz-Gerald & Fitz-Gerald, 1980, 1985; Shaul, 1981; Lytle, 1985) did not deal directly with AIDS, but document how Deaf youth are more likely to accept sexual myths, practice more risky sexual behaviors, and are less likely to use contraception in comparison to their hearing peers. By the 1990s, studies looked directly at the knowledge gap specifically related to HIV/AIDS. Gaps were demonstrated for all age groups including adolescents (Kleinig & Monhay, 1990; Luckner & Gonzales 1993; Baker-

Duncan, Dancer, Highly & Gibson, 1997), college students (Swartz 1993; Doyle 1995; Joseph, Sawyer & Desmond 1995; Svenson, Carmel & Varnhagen, 1997) and adults (Kennedy and Buchholz, 1995; Determan, Kordus & DeCarlo, 1999; Gaskins 1999). Work by Gannon (1998) and Getch and colleagues (Getch, Young & Denny, 1998; Getch, Branca, Fitz-Gerald & Fitz-Gerald, 2001) look more directly at the weaknesses of the sexuality education being offered to Deaf adolescents and adults. Despite this work and a little attention in the more popular press (Van Biema, 1994 in Time and Friess, 1998 in the HIV/AIDS magazine POZ), the gaps in information persist (Job, 2004; Mallison, 2004).

The gaps in sexuality education for Deaf youth are unacceptable. The opportunities for sexuality education need to be equivalent among Deaf and hearing students. The rise of risky sexual behaviors among Deaf students can be attributed to the lack of accurate knowledge and awareness of the severity of HIV/AIDS and other negative consequences. The estimated prevalence of HIV/AIDS in the local Washington, D.C. Deaf population is outrageously high. Instruction of sexuality education in a manner that is understood by Deaf students is a necessary requirement to reach the vulnerable young population.

Gallaudet University, the only liberal arts university in the world intended exclusively for Deaf and hard of hearing college students, provides one model for combating HIV/AIDS among Deaf youth. The university served 1,640 American and 190 international undergraduate and graduate students during the 2004–2005 academic year. Unlike at other universities, American Sign Language (ASL) is the method of communication among faculty, staff, and students, inside and outside of the classroom, so Deaf and hard of hearing students are able to fully experience college life in their own language and culture. Gallaudet's programs combating HIV/AIDS center on utilizing students as Peer Health Advocates (PHAs), allowing Gallaudet students to have access to HIV/AIDS information similar to hearing students at their universities.

Gallaudet's effort to prevent HIV/AIDS is coordinated by its Health and Wellness Programs (HWP). HWP's mission is to empower students to make informed health and lifestyle choices in accordance with their own values and belief systems. By supporting students on behavior and lifestyle change, HWP helps students become more successful members of the academic community. Since the majority of Deaf and hard of hearing college students obtain their sexuality and HIV/AIDS information from their peers, formal peer health education is an effective method to spread accurate information. Trained PHAs serve as representatives of HWP as active role-models and educators on campus for their peers in formal and informal settings.

Communication of sexuality and HIV/AIDS information

The "division [between Deaf and hearing individuals] was sad before AIDS. Now it can be deadly" (Friess, 1998, p. 63). There are far less opportunities for Deaf students to receive sexuality and HIV/AIDS information in comparison to hearing students. Only a few studies have been conducted to research how sexual health is communicated to Deaf students, and the knowledge, attitudes, and behaviors of Deaf students in regards to sexual health in the United States. Many factors are involved in lack of communication or miscommunication of sexuality and HIV/AIDS information among the Deaf community. Language and culture differences play the largest part in the lack of accurate communicated sexuality information.

Deaf and hard of hearing individuals may feel disconnected from the general society, contributing to a sense of social isolation, resulting in limited knowledge and awareness of topics that are common information to hearing populations (Joseph, Sawyer & Desmond, 1995; Gannon, 1998). Cultural and linguistic factors contribute to the lower levels of knowledge about HIV/AIDS. Deaf individuals do not have equal access to sexuality and HIV/AIDS information in comparison to hearing individuals (Doyle, 1995). Deaf and hard of hearing individuals are less likely than hearing people to learn from conversation, books, and television (Kleinig & Monhay, 1990). Deaf adolescents only receive the visual images of television, possibly missing the complete meaning of the message (Job, 2004). News and informative television programs and media messages are often not captioned (Fitz-Gerald & Fitz-Gerald, 1985; Doyle, 1995) therefore are often misinterpreted by Deaf individuals who use visual communication, so the intended message, especially in regards to sexuality issues, may be misconstrued (Fitz-Gerald & Fitz-Gerald, 1985).

Written English is often a challenge for Deaf adolescents due to the fact that English is not their first language; ASL is their natural language (Joseph, Sawyer & Desmond, 1995; Gannon, 1998). The National Coalition of the Deaf Community and HIV reports that 70% of Deaf people consider ASL their first language and English as their second language (Friess, 1998). A large majority of Deaf adults read English at the fifth-grade level, although most of the printed materials about HIV/AIDS are written at a more advanced level. For materials used for sexuality and HIV/AIDS education, it is essential for them to be written at an appropriate literacy level for Deaf and hard of hearing individuals to understand the information (Gannon, 1998). Pamphlets emphasizing pictures instead of text are more appropriate for deaf adolescents (Baker-Duncan et al., 1997). Written materials about HIV/AIDS are not enough for Deaf or hearing populations as the sole source of information. Most hearing individuals also receive information from the car radio, telephone, television news, and even eavesdropping on others' conversations.

The CDC states Deaf individuals are estimated to be aware of only approximately 25% of the HIV prevention information that hearing individuals know (Friess, 1998). One common misapprehension is that some Deaf individuals believe that being HIV *positive* means that they do not have the virus (Van Biema, 1994; Friess, 1998; Mallinson, 2004). "It's difficult to get across the meaning of words such as *positive*, which in medical terminology has the opposite meaning from the traditional definition" (Friess, 1998, p. 63). Effective communication is a requirement to assist deaf individuals to fully understand crucial information about HIV/AIDS (Mallinson, 2004).

Deaf adolescents with hearing parents have a disadvantage in terms of communication. Hearing parents with Deaf youth do not always fully understand Deafness, Deaf culture, and ASL. As approximately 90% of Deaf adolescents are born to hearing parents, and most of these parents do not learn ASL, communication between parents and Deaf children, therefore, is limited and life lessons taught within the family unit related to sexuality are infrequent (Meyers and Bartee, 1992; Friess, 1998). Even if parents do become proficient in ASL, sexuality signs are not often learned, creating another barrier to discussions about sexual health (Shaul, 1981; Friess, 1998). If Deaf adolescents have Deaf parents, the parents also tend to be uninformed about HIV/AIDS, so are unable to educate their children about the correct facts and protective behaviors to avoid HIV infection. Deaf youth are not relying on parents for sexuality and HIV/AIDS information, and communication does not appear to be improving among Deaf adolescents and their families. If parents are not teaching their Deaf adolescents about HIV prevention and transmission, the schools must take on the responsibility to educate adolescents about sexuality and HIV/AIDS (Swartz, 1993; Friess, 1998).

Language differences may limit Deaf adolescents' understanding of sexuality education. For example, certain idiomatic expressions may not be appropriate approaches to teaching sexuality and health information as Deaf adolescents may not be able to understand them (Job, 2004). English slang terms such as "messing around", "fooling around", or "getting it on" cannot be translated word for word from English to ASL, therefore deaf individuals may not fully understand the meaning of the phrases. Limitations that Deaf students face in mainstream classrooms involve many misunderstandings due to inadequate interpreter skills or no interpreter for a teacher with poor signing skills, including not knowing the signs related to sexual behaviors and over-relying on fingerspelling (Swartz, 1993; Friess, 1998; Gannon, 1998; Determan, 1999). Values or embarrassment about the topic by the interpreter may also influence or alter the translation of these sensitive topics (Gannon, 1998). While these factors are mostly linguistic in nature, communication about sexuality also takes place within a unique Deaf cultural environment.

The United States Deaf community is tightly knit with a high degree of physical and emotional intimacy, so Deaf individuals often feel more comfortable discussing more sensitive topics. The Deaf community has an interconnected network throughout the U.S. with their own social organizations and cultural institutions (Ries, 1994). Deaf individuals choose to be a member of the Deaf community, not necessarily based on their degree of hearing loss or geographic location, but for the sense of identity.

Due to the visual manner of ASL communication and the cultural norm of the American Deaf community, sexuality is often the topic of very open and direct discussion (Determan et al., 1999). Because the Deaf community is so tightly knit, information spreads rapidly. Confidentiality is often an issue because of the close relationships and the common "grapevine" in the community, so discussing sensitive issues, such as HIV/AIDS, is a serious concern for many Deaf individuals (Doyle, 1995; Kennedy & Buchholz, 1995). Anonymity and mistrust of health educators, service providers, and the use of interpreters makes Deaf individuals reluctant to be tested or to receive preventive health care or treatment (Friess, 1998; Determan, 1999). Because of privacy concerns, Deaf individuals are most often diagnosed with HIV when they begin to have complications or illnesses due to the virus. The delay of determining their HIV status and receiving treatment from lack of knowledge and comprehension of HIV/AIDS result in HIV-positive Deaf individuals dying earlier than hearing patients (Van Biema, 1994; Gaskins, 1999).

A written questionnaire was administered to Deaf adolescent students by Luckner and Gonzales (1993) to ascertain their knowledge and opinions in regards to HIV and AIDS. The 204 Deaf secondary students included in the study attended day programs and residential schools in the Rocky Mountain region of the United States. The students were misinformed about a large number of the knowledge-based items on the questionnaire. 70% of Deaf adolescents did not know that HIV/AIDS could not be contracted by donating blood. 62% of Deaf students did not realize that married people could get HIV/AIDS. The misconception that heterosexuals could not become infected with HIV was held by 46% of Deaf adolescent students, and 43% thought all homosexuals have HIV/AIDS.

Baker-Duncan, Dancer, Gentry, Highly and Gibson (1997) surveyed adolescents at five state schools for the Deaf in the United States to determine their knowledge of HIV/AIDS. There were 129 students in total from grades 9–12 that participated in the study. The questionnaire divided the knowledge questions into three levels, following the results of the survey: Obtained Knowledge, Emerging Knowledge, and No Knowledge. The majority of the students fell into the Emerging Knowledge category. The results found that only 8 of 35 basic HIV/AIDS questions were answered correctly by most of the Deaf students; the youth had a substantial deficit of fundamental HIV/AIDS knowledge. For example, they were not knowledgeable about who was susceptible to contract HIV/AIDS, as evident from many of their uncertain responses. The youth were unsure if only homosexuals contract HIV, if all homosexuals have HIV/AIDS, if heterosexuals could contract the virus, or even if high school students (themselves) could contract HIV. In addition, methods of protection against contracting HIV, such as using condoms and changing sexual behaviors, were unclear to Deaf adolescents.

College students also show these gaps. A comparative study of sexual health knowledge conducted by Swartz (1993) showed that Deaf college freshmen were considerably less knowledgeable in regards to sexuality in comparison to hearing college freshmen. Deaf students scored lowest on items related to anatomy and physiology sexuality knowledge.

The results from a questionnaire especially developed for Deaf students (Doyle, 1995) indicated that many Deaf college students are practicing risky sexual behaviors, despite some general knowledge about HIV/AIDS. 77% of the students reported having sex within the last three years. Of these students, 85% had sexual intercourse during their most recent sexual encounter, though only 50% of the students that had recent sexual intercourse used a condom. Approximately 50% of the Deaf students knew someone infected with HIV/AIDS. This may be an indicator that the incidence of HIV/AIDS among the Deaf community is high.

Results of a survey administered by Joseph, Sawyer and Desmond (1995) to 134 Deaf and hard of hearing college students were consistent with other current research. The Deaf and hard of hearing college students surveyed were not well informed about sexuality health issues, and students did not have a high correct response rate to knowledge questions regarding HIV/AIDS and safer sex behaviors. Deaf and hard of hearing college students in this study were also practicing high risk sexual behaviors that increased their risk of unplanned pregnancies and HIV infection. The majority (81%) of the college students reported being sexually active, and 43% reported having more than four sexual partners. Intercourse was initiated before the age of 18 among 65% of the students. Only 34% of the students reported using a condom during their most recent sexual encounter, and withdrawal was the most commonly practiced method of contraception (45%).

In terms of contraception, Sawyer and colleagues (1996) found hearing students (44%) were more likely to use condoms than Deaf students (30%), more likely to use birth control pills (34% versus 15%), and less likely to use the withdrawal method (13% versus 41%). Chosen methods of contraception may be due to levels of sexuality education and barriers of communicating with health care providers. Only one third of the students in both groups had ever been tested for HIV. Sources of health information differed a great deal for the Deaf and hearing college students. Deaf students received their sexuality information more often than hearing students from friends (85% versus 67%), workshops (40% versus 9%), and posters (30% versus 18%). Hearing students (79%) received their sexuality information more often than Deaf students (61%) from their doctors. Friends of Deaf college students that sign, workshops designed for Deaf students in ASL or with interpreters, and visual posters are important sources of information for Deaf students.

As Goldstein, Eckhardt, Joyner and Berry (this volume) demonstrate, these problems continue into adulthood. Goldstein et al.'s study of 452 signing Deaf adults show that many have significant gaps in their knowledge, including that 23% considered HIV to be a 'hearing person's disease'. Perlman and Leon's work (this volume) with 81 adults in the Chicago area shows, however, that participants benefited from a Deaf-focused educational intervention.

Although some research has been conducted to determine the knowledge, attitudes, and behaviors of Deaf students, follow-up studies and interventions have not been performed to improve and enhance the education of Deaf students. Reasons as to why Deaf students practice increased risky sexual behaviors can only be assumed to be linked to deficiencies in education about sexuality and HIV/AIDS. Two decades of studies have been conducted, but there has not been a documented change over time in the knowledge, attitudes, and behaviors of Deaf students due to a lack of further research from the results found from previous studies. The findings indicate that sexuality and HIV/AIDS education is needed for Deaf students to increase their knowledge and awareness of sexuality and HIV/AIDS issues. The outcomes of these studies show a dire need for Deaf students to receive adequate and effective sexuality and HIV/AIDS education to promote behavior changes.

This work on knowledge of HIV/AIDS documents the consequences of

Deaf people not having access to adequate information in their own language, but that timely interventions do work. In the next sections, studies of the programs meant to combat the knowledge gap among Deaf youth in the United States will be discussed and Gallaudet's Peer Health Advocate program will be offered as one model for how such education can be done. PHAs use the strengths of Deaf culture such as the ability to discuss sexuality topics directly and frankly, the tight-knit nature of the community, and the norm of turning to peers for information to help bridge the gap in a range of innovative ways.

Sexuality and HIV/AIDS education

There is not a great deal of literature that targets Deaf and hard of hearing adolescents and young adults in regards to sexuality and HIV/AIDS education. Much of the literature that has reviewed sexuality and HIV/AIDS education among Deaf and hard of hearing adolescent students is long out-dated. The most comprehensive studies (Fitz-Gerald & Fitz-Gerald, 1980, 1985; Shaul, 1981; Lytle, 1985; Luckner & Gonzales, 1993; Swartz, 1993; Doyle, 1995; Joseph et al., 1995; Sawyer et al., 1996; Baker-Duncan et al., 1997; Getch et al., 1998) were conducted in the 1980s and 1990s, so close to a decade has passed without an increase of published literature about sexuality and HIV/AIDS education among Deaf and hard of hearing adolescents. A few studies reviewed the content of sexuality education that has been taught in the schools, and some studies have surveyed the knowledge and behaviors of the students. However, there have not been follow-up studies to determine if there have been changes in the school environments to improve the sexuality and HIV/AIDS education for the Deaf and hard of hearing adolescent students in recent years (Determan et al., 1999). The HIV/AIDS epidemic only continues to grow among this age group and this population, though the literature does not reflect the importance of studying this high-risk adolescent subpopulation.

Studies in the 1980s documented problems with informal and formal sexuality education rather than HIV/AIDS education. Fitz-Gerald and Fitz-Gerald (1980; 1985) developed a framework to examine how Deafness influences the process of obtaining sexual health information. Deaf adolescents do not tend to receive their sexuality education at home or in school. Peers and experience were the most common methods to learn about sexual health issues for Deaf youth, though the information received from peers was found to be highly inaccurate (Fitz-Gerald & Fitz-Gerald, 1980, 1985). A great deal of sexuality education is learned through the "hidden curriculum" among Deaf and hard of hearing youth. Sexual experience and experimentation are often ignored by the staff of Deaf residential schools (Lytle, 1985); therefore, sexual feelings and interactions with sexual partners are not fully understood. As a result, adolescents' immaturity and impulsiveness in regards to sexuality may lead to detrimental consequences, such as mental anguish, unplanned pregnancy (Shaul, 1981), and HIV infection. More recent studies also show peers receiving inaccurate information from each other (Swartz, 1993; Gannon, 1998).

One reason for the importance of informal peer education is that little time has been spent on formal sexuality health education in Deaf schools because it has been viewed as less academic than other courses by the educators in these schools (Kleinig & Mohay, 1990). Few public or private institutions for Deaf and hard of hearing youth provide HIV/AIDS education for their students (Doyle, 1995). Information gaps about HIV prevention and transmission among Deaf adolescents have been found in previous studies (Gaskins, 1999).

For those schools that do teach sexuality education, the quality is questionable, the focus short-term, and education primarily occurs as a result of a crisis situation (Fitz-Gerald & Fitz-Gerald, 1985). Interpreters used in classes may not know the specific ASL sexuality signs or be able to clearly explain the full details that are being taught to the class about sexuality. Gaskins (1999) found that even some Deaf college students who had some HIV/AIDS education did not change their risky sexual behaviors based on their limited knowledge of HIV/AIDS. Deaf students are not connecting their knowledge of HIV/AIDS with their sexual behaviors (Doyle, 1995).

Getch and colleagues (1998) conducted a survey by mail of sexuality education curricula, materials and programs at 96 Deaf schools that use sign language in the United States (76% were returned). Administrators and teachers were questioned about the types and quality of the sexuality curricula, the amount of time the teachers spent modifying the material to be useful for Deaf youth, and the demographics of the sexuality teachers. The results showed that 13% of schools did not have any form of sexuality curricula. Many of the sexuality teachers were female, which does not provide many role-models for the male youth to discuss their emotional and physical changes, although is an advantage for Deaf females to have role-models with whom they can comfortably discuss sensitive sexuality issues. The students communicated mainly in ASL, and most of the teachers signed for themselves without interpreters. The sexuality education classes were small, with an average of about eight students.

Materials used to teach the sexuality lessons were most often texts and workbooks with a large number of words versus pictures and visuals. This method of education is not in the students' primary language, so many sexuality issues may be misunderstood. 94% of the teachers spent a great deal of time modifying the sexuality curricula prior to teaching the Deaf youth (Getch et al., 1998). Often, the sexuality curricula was taught within another class, so may have been covered in only one class period, which is not enough time to have full discussions on all the essential subjects within sexuality that may arise for Deaf youth.

As Perlman and Leon (this volume) demonstrate, however, effective programs can assist in raising awareness and therefore help to prevent HIV/AIDS. One example of a successful sexuality and HIV/AIDS education program can be seen in Los Angeles, California. AIDS Education Services for the Deaf assisted in the development of an explicit sexuality program for the California School for the Deaf in Riverside. This innovative curriculum displays condoms and graphic pictures to teach the students about HIV/AIDS through visual modes of education. Safer sex practices and skills are taught to the Deaf students to prevent HIV infection (Friess, 1998).

Another comprehensive program is Gallaudet's Peer Health Advocate (PHA) program. Peer education was reported as the most common method to learn about sexual health issues in the Deaf community. Including peers in the teaching process of other youth is one of the most effective methods of disseminating accurate information to Deaf and hard of hearing adolescents. Peer health education programs train students to become informed leaders in the student population to teach health knowledge and skills, and enhance the learning of sexuality and HIV/AIDS information by improving the communication channels of education (Joseph et al., 1995). Peer education is a key component in sexuality education; educating the student leaders in the Deaf community spreads accurate information and promotes safer sexual behaviors (Gannon, 1998). Trained peer health educators are effective in empowering Deaf adolescents and young adults about HIV/AIDS (Baker-Duncan et al., 1997).

Gallaudet's Peer Health Advocate education program

Gallaudet University's Health and Wellness Programs (HWP) were created in 1991. Gallaudet has approximately 2,000 students each year (1,830 during the 2004–2005 academic year) that the Peer Health Advocates (PHAs) target by a variety of means. Each year the number of PHAs ranges from five to seven with one Senior PHA or Graduate Assistant. Many students at Gallaudet University have stated in evaluations or by word-of-mouth that HWP has become much more visible than in previous years. The programs are larger-scale and many more students are attending the programs than in the past. For example, with the new affiliation with the First-Year Experience program within the past three years, they have begun to be able to require that the first-year students attend a number of the PHA programs. The incoming class is estimated to be about 300 students each year, and often at the beginning of the year, the PHA programs have 200–250 students attending the events.

The Peer Health Advocates

PHAs are paraprofessionals on the Gallaudet University campus, and have highly regarded positions in which many students compete to be accepted each year. There are a large number of qualifications and requirements for the job, so those five to seven students that are selected each year as PHAs, out of an estimated 20–25 applications, are deemed as leaders in the Gallaudet University community. Each year, one second-year PHA is selected as a Senior PHA or Graduate Assistant PHA as an especially high honor. PHAs in the past have been both genders, all sexual orientations, and a variety of ethnicities. A great deal of hard work is required from the PHAs for $8 per hour for approximately 20 hours per week. The PHAs are expected to place the job as a second priority to their academic work. The general responsibility of the PHAs is to remain focused on the goals specific to HWP of educating, advocating, and expanding health and wellness services and information to Gallaudet University students, and often faculty and staff.

PHAs are, in a sense, train-the-trainer types of positions. Experts from the health field train the PHAs, so the PHAs can disseminate accurate health information to the other students on campus.

The PHAs receive one week of intensive training at the beginning of the fall semester and another week at the beginning of the spring semester and ongoing instruction throughout the year to learn the educational information they need to present to their peers. Weekly meetings allow for program planning, feedback, and additional training to ensure accurate information is being taught on campus by the PHAs. Trainings include educational sessions, activities, and teambuilding to enhance the knowledge of the PHAs and the group dynamics. Educational sessions are presented to increase the knowledge base of the PHAs for a variety of health topics, then skills activity sessions assist in the process of understanding and formatting the information for the PHAs to teach the other students on campus. Teambuilding occurs through physical challenges and group problem solving exercises on the ropes course, in addition to other trust and open communication activities.

Experts from the health field at Gallaudet University and in the Washington, D.C. metropolitan area, Deaf and hearing, are invited to train the PHAs during their fall and spring intensive trainings. The organizations teach sexuality information to the PHAs from the viewpoint of their target population and explain the services they offer, so PHAs can refer students to these resources. The training is taught by educators in ASL or interpreted by qualified Gallaudet University staff into ASL if the hearing expert is unable to sign.

A number of different organizations provide professional training and resource materials to HWP and the PHAs. Deaf professionals from the HIV/AIDS department of Deaf-REACH (Referral, Education, Advocacy, Counseling, and Housing) teach the PHAs about safer sex education from the Deaf and hard of hearing individual's perspective. Deaf-REACH also provides HIV testing and counseling to Gallaudet University. The Deaf Abused

Women's Network (DAWN) has Deaf advocates that act as a support system to Deaf and hard of hearing survivors that have experienced sexual assault. A 24-hour TTY hotline is also offered by DAWN as a service for Deaf and hard of hearing individuals. The Rape, Abuse, and Incest National Network (RAINN) is currently developing a national sexual assault online hotline that will be the nation's first secure online crisis hotline providing live help. This service will be an effective anonymous and convenient mode of communication for Deaf individuals to receive support following sexual assault. The Superior Court of the District of Columbia houses the Domestic Violence Intake Center that handles domestic violence cases in the Washington, D.C. area. Advocates for Youth teaches adolescents about sexual health and safer sex to prevent HIV/AIDS, sexually transmitted infections (STIs), and pregnancy through a realistic and positive approach. Planned Parenthood offers affordable reproductive and sexuality education, health clinics, and services to women, men, and adolescents. The D.C. Rape Crisis Center has volunteers that can assist individuals through the after-effects of rape by accompanying survivors to the hospital, self-defense classes, individual and group counseling, and a 24-hour TTY hotline for Deaf and hard of hearing individuals. The Whitman-Walker Clinic educates about HIV/AIDS prevention through outreach education in the community and has a clinic for testing and treatment services.

Trainings provide the PHAs with a foundation to build upon throughout the year to accomplish their job to the best of their ability. The PHAs have many specific job responsibilities, including peer support, team member, administrative, and outreach roles. Peer support responsibilities include a focus on confidentiality for all issues regarding student information, one-on-one interaction skills, and resource and referral knowledge. Team member responsibilities include remaining a role-model on campus for other students 24-hours a day, seven days a week, complying with university policies, and aligning the PHA position as a priority above personal commitments. Administrative responsibilities include utilizing program planning and evaluation tools, sharing responsibilities with other PHAs, materials research and development, marketing for the diverse individuals on campus, attending mandatory intensive and weekly trainings, and end of training and semester evaluations. The outreach responsibilities are quite extensive, and include program and health booth planning and presentation, program evaluation and summary, one-on-one sessions, peer program feedback evaluations, bulletin boards, bathroom tips, special events, health fairs, dramatic performances, role-plays, activities, newsletters, and collaboration with departments and organizations on- and off-campus. Bathroom tips are eye-catching and sometimes controversial flyers on the back of restroom stall doors to catch the attention of the students.

PHAs are also involved with informal teaching of sexuality and HIV/AIDS education on Gallaudet University's campus. Many students view the PHAs as knowledgeable role-models that lead by example. PHAs are selected for their leadership skills and ability to guide others, but are also open to learning from their interactions with others. Often, students approach PHAs after presentations, in dorms, off-campus, or in class to ask questions about specific health issues, especially related to sexuality. Students who have been sexually assaulted sometimes come forward to discuss their situation, or students will ask for clarification about sexuality information they have heard in class or from their friends.

The finding that the majority of sexuality education comes from peers among Deaf and hard of hearing students at Gallaudet University is reinforced by the evaluations collected after the PHAs have taught sexuality and HIV/AIDS programs, indicating that HWP is reaching the college students, increasing their knowledge of sexual health and HIV/AIDS, and has an effective health education program. The evaluations state that Gallaudet University students feel that they are more knowledgeable about sexuality issues following a PHA program, are very interested in the subject matter, feel the visual presentations are excellent, feel comfortable to discuss sexuality issues with the PHAs, and that PHA sexuality programs should be repeated in the future.

The programs
The Gallaudet University campus community is reached by a variety of individual, group, and community-wide health education strategies. Drop-in appointments for students to talk one-on-one with a PHA or to obtain free condoms are available during regular office hours. As visual education is a necessity to reach the Deaf and hard of hearing college students and make an

impact on their lives, the programming presented by the PHAs includes PowerPoint presentations, pictures, models, videos, brochures, and activities to meet the needs of the Deaf and hard of hearing students. Often, HWP collaborates with other Gallaudet University departments to cosponsor events, such as movies, speakers, panels, and health fairs. In the past, HWP has collaborated with Judicial Affairs, Multicultural Student Programs, Mental Health Center, Orientation Programs, Community Service Programs, Campus Activities, Campus Life, Student Health Services, and the Department of Public Safety. With some encouragement and guidance from the Coordinator, the PHAs initiate creative, innovative ideas that allow HWP to continue to offer interesting and captivating programs. The PHAs teach on a variety of sexuality health topics including, sexual responsibility, healthy relationships, safer sex, sexual assault, STIs, and HIV/AIDS. All of the programs offered provide factual information, discussions, and an activity to apply the newly learned information to the students' lives about each health topic.

Prior to the beginning of each academic year, the PHAs perform straightforward dramatized skits, short scenarios, for the New Student Orientation. The skits focus on topics including, multiple sexual partners, safer sex by negotiating condom use with partners, HIV and STI testing with partners, the window period for HIV, partner trust and cheating, heterosexual and homosexual relationships, and date rape at a house party.

One example of a skit is *The Big Bed*:

One large bed is in the middle of the stage. A couple pops out from under the covers.

Woman (pushing man away): I think we should talk about our past partners before we go any further.

Man: Ok, but I don't really think it's necessary. I have been pretty safe, and I assume you have been too. Right?

Woman: (nods)

Man: So, what do you want to know?

Woman: Well, I just wanted you to know that I've only been with one other man, and I was faithful to him, and I'm sure that he was faithful to me. What about you?

Man: Well, I've had a few more partners than you......hmmmm......let me think......

Woman (getting angry): What do you mean, 'let me think'?

Man: Well, there was Sarah......

Sarah (comes onto stage and jumps into bed with the couple): Hi! Because I had sex with him, you will be having sex with me too. But, don't worry. I was a virgin before him, and I never cheated on him.

Man: And there was Kim......

Kim (comes onto stage and jumps into bed with the couple): Hey, what's up? I had one partner before him, Doug, so you will be having sex with both of us too.

Doug comes walking onto stage and jumps into bed too, waving hi!...

Man: And there was a time that I experimented with my friend John......

John (walks onto stage over to the bed and jumps in): Hi cutie......I missed you.

Man (to John): Me too......how have you been? But, I'm with her now (pointing to his current partner).

Man turns back to woman.

Woman: Oh my gosh! So, technically I am not just going to be sleeping with you, but I am going to be sleeping with at least four other people! And who knows who Doug and John had sex with!

Man: Well, before I had sex with each of them, we waited six months, then got tested for STIs and HIV, and I used protection every time with all of my partners.

Woman: Yeah, well, since I have only been with one other person, and he had only been with me, after a while we decided not to use condoms anymore.

Man: And you're sure he was only with you?

Woman: Of course! He was very honest with me.

Woman's previous partner (walks onto stage and jumps into bed with everyone): Hey honey! You know, there's something that I've been meaning to tell you.

Woman: Yeah?

Woman's previous partner: Well, remember that time you went on vacation for a month with your family? Well, I got bored, so I hooked up with your friend Jennifer.

Woman (shocked): Jennifer? You mean the one with HIV? What? Why? I can't believe you didn't tell me!

Woman's previous partner: Well, you were the one that I cared about then. She meant nothing. She didn't know she had it then, and it was only one time......I'm sorry. I didn't know how to tell you......

(Everyone looks at one another with shocked looks on their faces.)

The scene goes dark.

Introducing these sensitive topics by way of the PHAs to the approximately 300 new first-year students establishes a connection between the students. When the first-year students have questions regarding sexuality and HIV/AIDS issues, they will be more likely to seek out a PHA to discuss these issues because they will be familiar with the fact that PHAs are knowledgeable peers.

He Said/She Said is the first PHA program of each year and is always our most popular event. Attendance tends to be approximately three-quarters of the First-Year students. The females and males give their own perspectives about scenarios that are displayed about sexual misconduct situations that may occur on campus. Rules to respect opinions are given prior to the scenarios, and there are a few representatives from each gender for each scenario to explain their perspective of the sexual misconduct situation. Also, during the first month of the academic year, a safer sex program is presented about facts, activities, such as condom demonstrations, and discussion about how to practice safer sex behaviors and apply those newly learned skills to the students' lives. To advertise the program in previous years, PHAs wearing a sign labeled with the HIV virus chased a college student in the cafeteria, then the "Condom Lady" wearing condoms stuck to her clothes and a large latex condom hat saved the college student by giving her a condom to use during sexual activity.

Every two weeks during the academic year, confidential HIV testing is offered by Deaf-REACH. The individuals who provide the HIV tests and counseling are Deaf, so communication during this sensitive process can be clearly understood. Loads of free condoms are given out to the students to make safer sex fun and encourage the use of condoms if students are sexually active. Studded, ribbed, colored, glow-in-the-dark, flavored, and multi-colored condoms and informational brochures targeting the Deaf and hard of hearing college students on campus are made available by Deaf-REACH. Some students do not feel comfortable getting tested at Gallaudet University due to the tight knit relationships of the Deaf community, so Deaf-REACH also provides HIV testing at their local main office in Washington, D.C.

Throughout the year, HWP plans programs based on national awareness weeks and months. December 1, for example, is World AIDS Day, so that day tends to be full of HIV/AIDS-related activities. The PHAs have health booths to give out information about HIV/AIDS and free condoms, and there are presentations about how HIV/AIDS can affect one's life, and an AIDS Walk supported by the President of Gallaudet University, I. King Jordan. In the evening, movies about AIDS, such as *And the Band Played On*, are shown and followed by a discussion about the film.

Valentine's Day, February 14, is National Condom Day. PHAs have health booths including trivia and condom races on dildos, walking distribution of free condoms for students, and visits from the "Condom Lady" in a latex condom hat. February has one week that is designated as Sexual Responsibility Week. Past programs have included focus on healthy relationships, communication with partners to discuss sexuality, safer sex, and each partner's sexual intentions within the relationship. STI awareness has included programs such as an STI gallery for students to identify pictures of various STIs and opportunistic infections of HIV/AIDS. The students always enjoy sexual jeopardy with headers such as Anything Goes, HIV/AIDS, Contraception, and STIs. Another activity also used in programs had students rank sexual behaviors as low-, moderate-, and high-risk practices, such as vaginal sex with a condom, anal sex without a condom, fondling, massaging, and mutual masturbation.

The "Can I Kiss You?" program by Mike Domitrz was brought to the university for April, Sexual Assault Awareness Month. The presentation focused on asking permission prior to initiating any sexual behaviors with a partner, and was well-attended by over 200 staff and students. The D.C. Rape Crisis Center has come to Gallaudet University during the month of April to teach self-defense programs to students to protect themselves against stranger attacks. Health booths have provided resource information from Men Can Stop Rape, D.C. Rape Crisis Center, and DAWN. During the 2002–2003 academic year, the PHAs developed a sexual misconduct video depicting subtle and explicit scenarios from sexual harassment to sexual assault. The PHAs unveiled their video at the Washington, D.C. Peer Exchange with local college and university peer health education programs in attendance. The following year, the PHAs showed the video of their New Student Orientation skit performance, as described in detail above.

As with all programs, needs assessment research is vital. The Core Survey has been conducted periodically at Gallaudet University to inquire about students' sexual behaviors, as well as alcohol and drug use behaviors. Educational health programming is then targeted to the specific needs of the Gallaudet University students. The results can even be compared to anonymous schools selected by the Core Institute that are similar to Gallaudet University to determine our students' behaviors in relation to those of other college students in the United States.

The Core Survey was conducted in 1995, 1997, and 2004 at Gallaudet University (Core Institute). Results that specifically pertain to sexuality issues have been reported in this paper. Of the Gallaudet University students that were surveyed, 61% (1995), 57% (1997), and 66% (2004) reported engaging in sexual intercourse within the past year. There were 14% (1995), 8% (1997), and 6.5% (2004) of Gallaudet University students that experienced forced sexual touching or fondling. 13% (1995), 6% (1997), and 7.3% (2004) of Gallaudet students experienced unwanted sexual intercourse. While under the influence of alcohol or drugs, Gallaudet students have reported being taken advantage of sexually, 17% (1995), 11% (1997), and 14% (2004), and have taken advantage of another sexually, 10% (1995), 5% (1997), and 6% (2004). Gallaudet students felt there was a "great risk" associated if students regularly engaged in unprotected sexual activity with a single partner, 52% (1995), 57% (1997), and 53% (2004), and also if students regularly engaged in unprotected sexual activity with multiple partners, 66% (1995), 68% (1997), and 84% (2004).

There was a rise in Gallaudet University students that engaged in sexual intercourse, but the sexual assault rates have decreased, and the attitudes towards risky sexual behaviors have improved. The sexuality education efforts that have been implemented through the HWP office seem to be changing some students' behaviors and attitudes, so the PHAs will continue to teach sexuality and HIV/AIDS information to the Deaf student population, and enhance our programs in the future with new, innovative educational strategies.

Future research and practice

HWP has developed many innovative sexual health ideas that will be implemented in the near future to reach the Deaf and hard of hearing college students at Gallaudet University. New collaborative efforts will be promoted to expand HWP and enhance the programs offered by the PHAs. To improve program development and presentation, updated resources are needed for the PHAs to plan programs, as well as materials to use to reinforce presentation information. Additional visual resources that would be applicable to HWP include updated videos, books, brochures, training and educational materials, computer programs, props and costumes for educational dramatized skits, and prepackaged educational materials and packets. For the Deaf and hard of hearing students to visualize the health impact of behaviors, display materials and information boards with photographs and pictures would improve current educational strategies. For programs and trainings, inviting guest speakers more frequently to personally impact the students, such as an HIV-positive Deaf individual to talk to the Gallaudet University student body, would influence the college students' decisions and sexual behaviors.

The Sexual Misconduct Response Protocol and Procedures manual has recently been developed for Gallaudet University; the manual will be finalized by the committee of Judicial Affairs, Student Development Programs, Campus Life, Dean's Office of Student Affairs, Mental Health Center, and the Department of Public Safety in the near future. The manual will act as a guide for faculty and staff to refer students that have experienced sexual misconduct to the appropriate resources. This protocol is necessary to keep all students on the Gallaudet University campus within the university's care if any undesirable incidents were to occur. Any faculty and staff member within the campus may be involved in acting as a confidant or support system for a student.

In the Fall of 2004, HWP received $15,600 from the Health and Human Services Office of Women's Health and Matthews Media Group, Inc. for a project regarding Deaf female adolescents and health issues that affect their lives. The project was initiated with two college-aged female focus groups with eight to ten females in each group at Gallaudet University to determine their health education needs during their high school years. Sexuality was found to be the predominant subject for which the Deaf and hard of hearing women felt they needed more information. Development of a pilot peer health education program for Deaf high school students at the Model Secondary School for the Deaf (MSSD) on Gallaudet University's campus is the next phase in implementing the findings from the focus groups. The new peer health education program will be based on the HWP model that is already successful on the college-level at Gallaudet University. When the peer education program starts at MSSD, the current PHAs in the Gallaudet University HWP department will be the key trainers of the high school PHAs. Modifying the current Gallaudet PHA program for high school students will be a necessary part of the development process of the MSSD PHA program. Following successful implementation, similar programs to the MSSD model can then be developed throughout the United States, so Deaf and hard of hearing high school students can obtain the necessary sexual health information for them to live safe and healthy adult lives.

HWP quite successfully employs the PHAs to teach sexuality and HIV/AIDS education at Gallaudet University to Deaf and hard of hearing college students. The in-depth training and superior work ethic of the PHAs result in their strong presence as educators among their peers on Gallaudet University's campus. The variety of programming initiatives gives a broad array of approaches to reach most of the 2,000 Deaf and hard of hearing students in the campus community. Specific strategies for future directions proposed by HWP will motivate and drive the Coordinator, to follow-through and fulfill the plans so that the PHAs will be even more effective in teaching sexuality and HIV/AIDS education at Gallaudet University.

In order to reach Deaf adolescents and decrease their risk of HIV infection, numerous steps are required to meet their specific needs. Future research needs to assess the linguistic and cultural differences of acquiring and internalizing sexuality and HIV/AIDS information among Deaf adolescents and young adults. Sexuality curricula and resources for younger Deaf students that are accessible and understood are still needed, and other barriers need to be identified and removed (Doyle, 1995; Sawyer et al., 1996; Gannon, 1998; Getch et. al, 1998). Resolving discrepancies in sexuality knowledge and bridging the gap of information for deaf adolescents is a priority. Evaluation of the few current sexuality and HIV/AIDS education programs that are offered at this time to Deaf adolescents across the country needs to be conducted. Guidelines can then be developed from the findings to conduct further research and create more effective sexuality and HIV/AIDS education programs (Swartz, 1993). The successful components of these programs can be replicated throughout the United States to reach all Deaf and hard of hearing students (Determan et al., 1999). Knowledge alone may not change behaviors, but it is a suggested starting point to increase awareness of important sexual health issues. Sexuality and HIV/AIDS education must be age, language, and culture-appropriate to reach the Deaf and hard of hearing adolescents. Adapting a currently available sexuality education curriculum to deaf students may be the best approach to developing a sexuality program for Deaf and hard of hearing adolescent students (Joseph et al., 1995).

More time needs to be spent to educate Deaf youth about sexuality issues in school settings because this may be their only method of learning about sexual health topics. It is critical that Deaf youth receive correct facts by an educational institution in order to make informed decisions, stay safe, and have healthy relationships. It is much easier to develop a healthy lifestyle opposed to breaking unhealthy habits in the future. Taking responsibility for actions comes with increased knowledge of risk behaviors and healthy behaviors and decreases the risks of HIV/AIDS (Getch et. al, 1998; Job 2004). With the valuable information that has been learned from previous studies and from Gallaudet University's HWP, sexuality and HIV/AIDS education can be more effectively targeted to meet the needs of Deaf adolescents and young adults in the future. Gallaudet University's HWP can be used as a model to expand upon what has been learned through experience to reach Deaf youth in the United States and around the world.

References

Baker-Duncan, N., Dancer, J., Gentry, B., Highly, P., & Gibson, B. (1997). Deaf adolescents' knowledge of AIDS. Grade and gender effects. *American Annals for the Deaf, 142 (5),* 368–372.

Center for Disease Control and Prevention. (2002). *HIV/AIDS and adolescents and young adults.* Department of Health and Human Services, Office of HIV/AIDS Policy, The Leadership Campaign on AIDS.

Center for Disease Control and Prevention. (2004a). *Youth risk behavior surveillance – United States, 2003.* Morbidity and Mortality Weekly Report, 53 (SS-2).

Center for Disease Control and Prevention. (2004b). *Basic statistics.* National Center for HIV, STD and TB Prevention, Divisions of HIV/AIDS Prevention. Retrieved April 27, 2005, from http://www.cdc.gov/hiv/stats.htm

Core Institute. (1995, 1997, 2004). *Gallaudet University Core Alcohol and Drug Survey Long Form.* Southern Illinois University at Carbondale, Student Health Programs, Carbondale, Illinois.

Determan, B., Kordus, N., & DeCarlo, P. (1999). *What are Deaf persons' HIV prevention needs?* Center for AIDS Prevention Studies (CAPS) and the AIDS Research Institute, University of California, San Francisco.

Doyle, A. G. (1995). AIDS knowledge, attitudes and behaviors among Deaf college students: A preliminary study. *Sexuality and Disability, 13 (2),* 107–134.

Fitz-Gerald, M., & Fitz-Gerald, G. (1980). Sexuality and Deafness: An American overview. *British Journal of Sexual Medicine, 7,* 30–34.

Fitz-Gerald, M., & Fitz-Gerald, G. (1985). Information on sexuality: Where does it come from? In D. Fitz-Gerald & M. Fitz-Gerald (Eds.), *Viewpoints: Sex Education and Deafness.* Washington, D.C.: Gallaudet College, Pre-College Programs. 34–37.

Friess, S. (1998, April). Silence = Deaf. In the translation from English to sign language, HIV education loses something: lives. *POZ,* 60–63.

Gannon, C. L. (1998). The Deaf community and sexuality education. *Sexuality and Disability, 16 (4),* 283–292.

Gaskins, S. (1999). Special population: HIV/AIDS among the Deaf and hard of hearing. *Journal of the Association of Nurses in AIDS Care, 10 (2),* 75–78.

Getch, Y. Q., Young, M., & Denny, G. (1998). Sexuality education for students who are Deaf: Current practices and concerns. *Sexuality and Disability, 16 (4),* 269–280.

Getch, Y. Q., Branca, D. L., Fitz-Gerald, D., & Fitz-Gerald, M. (2001). A rationale and recommendations for sexuality education in schools for students who are Deaf. *American Annals for the Deaf, 146 (5),* 401–408.

Goldstein, M. F., Eckhardt, E., Joyner, P., & Berry, R. (this volume). An HIV knowledge and attitude survey of Deaf U.S. adults.

Job, J. (2004). Factors involved in the ineffective dissemination of sexuality information to individuals who are Deaf or hard of hearing. *American Annals of the Deaf, 149 (3),* 264–273.

Joseph, J. M., Sawyer, R., & Desmond, S. (1995). Sexual knowledge, behavior and sources of information among Deaf and hard of hearing college students. *American Annals of the Deaf, 140 (4),* 338–345.

Kennedy, S. G., & Buchholz, C. L. (1995). HIV and AIDS among the Deaf. *Sexuality and Disability, 13 (2),* 145–158.

Kleinig, D., & Monhay, H. (1990). A comparison of the health knowledge of hearing-impaired and hearing high school students. *American Annals of the Deaf, 135 (3),* 246–251.

Luckner, J. L., & Gonzales, B. R. (1993). What Deaf and hard-of-hearing adolescents know and think about AIDS. *American Annals of the Deaf, 138 (4),* 338–342.

Lytle, R. R. (1985). Growing up in a residential school: Developmental needs and school policies. In D. Fitz-Gerald, D. & M. Fitz-Gerald (Eds.), *Viewpoints: Sex Education and Deafness.* Washington, D.C.: Gallaudet College, Pre-College Programs. 29–33.

Mallinson, R. K. (2004). Deaf culture: When "positive" is a good thing. *Journal of the Association of Nurses in AIDS Care, 15 (4),* 21–22.

Meyers, J. E., & Bartee, J. W. (1992). Improvements in the signing of hearing parents of Deaf children. *American Annals of the Deaf, 137 (3),* 257–260.

Monaghan, L. (this volume). Maryland 2003 HIV infection statistics for hearing and Deaf populations: Analysis and policy suggestions.

Perlman, T. S., & Leon, S. C. (this volume). Preventing AIDS in the Midwest: The design and efficacy of culturally sensitive HIV/AIDS prevention education materials for Deaf communities.

Ries, R. W. (1994). *Prevalence and characteristics of persons with hearing trouble: United States, 1990-91.* National Center for Health Statitistics, Vital Health Stat. 10 (188).

Sawyer, R. G., Desmond, S. M., & Joseph, J. M. (1996). A comparison of sexual knowledge, behavior, and sources of health information between Deaf and hearing university students. *Journal of Health Education, 27 (3),* 144–152.

Shaul, S. (1981). Deafness and sexuality: A developmental review. *American Annals of the Deaf, 126 (4),* 432–438.

Svenson, L., Carmel, S., & Varnhagen, C. K. (1997). A review of the knowledge, attitudes and behaviours of university students concerning HIV/AIDS. *Health Promotion International, 12 (1),* 61–68.

Swartz, D. B. (1993). A comparative study of sex knowledge among hearing and Deaf college freshmen. *Sexuality and Disability, 11 (2),* 129–147.

Van Biema, D. (1994, April 4). AIDS and the Deaf. *Time Magazine, 143 (14),* 76-77.

Contact information
Gwendolyn Suzanne Roberts, MPH, CHES, RYT
Health and Wellness Programs Coordinator
Gallaudet University
Health and Wellness Programs
800 Florida Avenue, NE
Ely 103F
Washington, D.C. 20002
Tel: +1 202 651 5432
Fax: +1 202 651 5651
email: gwendolyn.roberts@gallaudet.edu

Preventing AIDS in the Midwest: The design and efficacy of culturally sensitive HIV/AIDS prevention education materials for Deaf communities

Toby S. Perlman and Scott C. Leon

Deaf Worlds
2006 | vol 22 (1)
Forest Books ©
ISSN 1362–3125

Key words

Deafness, HIV/AIDS, HIV prevention, health literacy, access to care, cultural sensitivity.

Abstract

Many Deaf adult Americans read at a level lower than the readability level of most health care materials. Health information presented verbally often confuses people with a significant hearing loss. It has been suggested that these written and verbal barriers contribute to lower HIV-related health knowledge in Deaf persons compared to hearing persons. This study explores the impact that a culturally sensitive prevention education presentation may have on a Deaf person's knowledge of and attitude towards HIV/AIDS. Eighty-one community-based Deaf adults completed an HIV/AIDS knowledge and attitude survey prior to and following an HIV prevention education presentation in American Sign Language. For each knowledge question, we created two groups: the participants who answered the questions incorrectly at pre-test and the participants who answered the questions correctly at pre-test. We next compared the two groups' post-test percent correct for each knowledge item to determine if the group with incorrect answers could catch up in knowledge with the correct answers group at post-test. Using a paired-samples t-test for attitude questions, we examined changes in health-promoting attitudes before and after the presentation. For nine out of ten knowledge questions and four out of five attitude questions, our sample benefited from the educational intervention.

Biographies

Toby S. Perlman received her Ph.D. in Clinical Psychology from Northwestern University Medical School in December, 1995. She is a licensed clinical psychologist and the Manager of the Deaf and Hard of Hearing Program at Advocate Illinois Masonic Behavior Health Services. She has over 15 years experience working for social service agencies that provide services to members of the Deaf community. In her current position, she has written and produced four health education videos in American Sign Language. The video on HIV/AIDS is entitled, "Ignore AIDS? CAN'T!".

Scott Leon received his Ph.D. in Clinical Psychology from Northwestern University Medical School in June, 2002. During his graduate studies, Scott developed research interests in mental health services evaluation. This research has focused on improving the efficacy of services delivered to youth and the development of models of improvement in psychotherapy for adults. Scott has worked with healthcare organizations, child welfare agencies, and community mental health providers to improve quality through outcomes management. In addition, Scott provides psychotherapy as an associate in a private group practice.

Introduction

The special communication and cultural needs of Deaf Americans are often unrecognized, dismissed, and/or ignored by the mainstream hearing population (Ebert & Heckerling, 1995; Barnett, 1999; Witte & Kuzel, 2000; Guthmann & Blozis, 2001; Health Resources and Services Administration, 2001; Steinberg, et al., 2002; Mallinson, 2004a). It is estimated that 10% of the people living in the United States have a significant hearing loss. The subpopulation of Deaf people who communicate in American Sign Language (ASL) and self-identify as sharing a sociolinguistic cultural connection, as opposed to a medical problem or disability, has been roughly estimated at about .14% (Mitchell, 2005; Mitchell, et al., 2006). The last study to formally examine this national statistic, however, occurred in 1972. The data was based on the National Census of the Deaf Population (NCDP) registry and examined how many respondents who were born deaf or experienced hearing loss before 19 years rated themselves as "good signers" (Schein & Delk, 1974). Throughout this paper, the word "Deaf" will be capitalized when referring to a person or group of people who identifies as being affiliated with American Deaf culture as it is described above; the lowercase spelling of "deaf" will identify a person or group of people with a significant hearing loss (Phillips, 1996).

The only demographic information available for Deaf persons residing in the Midwest is specific to the greater Chicagoland metropolitan area. The data from a health care survey completed by a group of 203 Deaf adults between November, 2002 and March, 2003 suggests that the Deaf residents of the Chicago area reflect a very diverse group (Margellos-Anast, et al., 2005). The respondents to this survey were not chosen randomly but they were recruited from a pool of over 1,000 patients who had been receiving services from the two largest Deaf and Hard of Hearing health care programs at multiple clinic and hospital locations spread throughout the city and suburbs. Although, unlike most Deaf Americans, the participants were connected to a culturally sensitive health care system, the data generated by this one health survey begins to suggest that Chicago's Deaf community represents a variety of ethnic/racial and socioeconomic backgrounds.

Survey participants were 18 years of age or older (mean age of 45 years old) and made their own health decisions (i.e., did not reside in a group home or have a legal guardian). The inclusion criteria also required that they either (1) self-reported that ASL was their primary mode of communication or (2) self-reported being proficient in ASL and either prelingually deaf or self-identified with the Deaf community. Fifty-six percent of the participants were Non-Hispanic White, 29% were Non-Hispanic Black, 10% were Hispanic and 6% were from other racial/ethnic groups. Thirty-four percent completed high school and 14% graduated college. Fifty-three percent earned less than $20,000 annually and 23% earned between $20,000 and $40,000 annually. Sixty-three percent reported a government-based source of health insurance and 39% reported an employer sponsored source of insurance. Because of rounding, not all percentages add up to 100 (Margellos-Anast, et al., 2005).

Here in the Midwest area, the majority of Deaf residents tend to use and prefer ASL for effective communication. As is true of most Deaf Americans, one can assume that most of these Deaf adults:

1. have grown up in hearing families in which ASL was not used or was used minimally and have struggled, therefore, to accumulate the health knowledge necessary to support healthy lifestyles and the successful navigation of the health care system (Neisser, 1990; Adams, 1997; Pollard, 1998);

2. have developed a reading comprehension level that often is significantly lower than the high school and above readability level of most American health care materials and, therefore, have been limited in their ability to utilize the written health and prevention information found in a doctor's office or other health care facilities (Phillips, 1996; McEwen, 1998; Rudd, 2003);

3. have experienced face-to-face provider-patient communication styles which may reduce "dialogues" to the back and forth writing of short phrases and/or may depend on the patients' oral/speech reading skills, both of which further compromise their comprehension of health care information and treatment recommendations (Ebert & Heckerling, 1995; Phillips, 1996).

Even if a Deaf adult were fortunate enough to have a certified sign language interpreter in the doctor's office with him or her, much of what American doctors present often is filled with medical terminology and complicated concepts. Frequently, the translation of a provider's words into a visual language does not significantly improve a Deaf patient's comprehension if the provider's discourse involves a complicated string of jargon and technical terms as is often true when the topic of discussion is HIV/AIDS. It would require significant amounts of the interpreter's time to expand on and exemplify the provider's medical vocabulary in a culturally and linguistically sensitive manner. The source of the problem, however, does not lie in the hands of the sign language interpreter but in the words of the provider. Having medical terms spelled out in ASL often is an insufficient attempt at creating a culturally sensitive environment. Provider communication that is based on both plain language and cultural sensitivity helps increase the chances that the provider–patient interaction will support healthy reactions on the part of the patient. Many providers, however, are unaware of and insensitive to the complexity of their communications (Rudd, 2003). For example, health care professionals who treat Deaf patients probably have encountered a Deaf person who reports being pleased and relieved to have learned in the past, through interpreted or written communication with a previous health care provider, that he or she was HIV "positive" (i.e., "good" or "well") and, therefore, not in need of medical treatment (Mallinson, 2004b). Adding the simple phrase, "and that means you have HIV inside your body," is one example of how providers can easily deconstruct the barricade of technical language that prevents a Deaf person from comprehending the serious consequences and treatment options associated with a diagnosis of being HIV positive.

There is a lack of consistent data related to the seroprevalence (the frequency that HIV antibodies are found in the blood serum) of Deaf Americans. However, the communication and accessibility barriers Deaf persons encounter combined with the higher rate of substance abuse their subpopulation experiences suggest that they may have a higher-than-average risk of contracting AIDS (Peinkofer, 1994; Gaskins, 1999; Health Resources and Services Administration, 2001). In America, two obstacles impede the development and dissemination of the linguistically and culturally sensitive HIV/AIDS education materials that are necessary to help reduce this high risk: the dearth of health educators with competencies in providing care to Deaf persons and the geographic characteristics of the Deaf community. Unlike most cultural and linguistic minority groups in American metropolitan areas, Deaf persons often live scattered throughout a city or town; there are no Deaf neighborhoods. The sense of community is based more on an emotional connectedness than a geographic neighborliness. The lack of skilled educators and the need to outreach throughout an extended geographic area, as opposed to establishing a neighborhood resource, further complicate the HIV prevention education process for the Deaf community. Finally, as with most cultural minorities, the educational resources already available to the general population require significant modifications to best meet the learning preferences and cultural values of the Deaf community and, because of the low incidence of deafness, the funding to support these modifications is scarce in the United States.

The learning preferences of Deaf Americans are easy to identify. Deaf

Americans value receiving information from friends or family via the face-to-face communication of American Sign Language. There is more trust in an external source of information if that source is a native signer who relies on storytelling, reenactment, and demonstration over factual description. Facial expression, body language and social connectedness are essential components to the meaning of information and the amount of respect given to it (Phillips, 1996).

Given these culturally based learning preferences, we developed a slide show presentation with a minimal amount of English words; it was presented to the Deaf community by native signers who had been trained in the area of HIV/AIDS prevention between October, 2001 and June, 2002. The presentation frequently expanded definitions of important English phrases (such as "viral load") and concepts (such as how medication works) through graphics, illustrations, participatory "games", and demonstrations. The primary educator and his two assistants were all very active within and highly respected by their Deaf community. The primary educator had experience organizing community activities and was sensitive to the community's attitude towards HIV/AIDS. From his perspective, the members of Chicago's Deaf community were extremely uncomfortable with the topic of HIV/AIDS and in many cases appeared to respond to the topic in a fashion more common with the general American public's response to the topic in the mid to late 1980s. Based on what he had encountered within his community, he described an environment in which many people were uninformed about the topic and uncomfortable with having it approached. It was decided, therefore, early in the process of developing the prevention education presentation to recruit participants with an emphasis on the social component of the event: allowing time before and after the presentation to meet with friends, providing refreshments, including participatory activities and choosing locations for the presentations that already had been identified as social gathering places. Additionally, before marketing the presentation to the Deaf community at large, the educator had provided the presentation to a group of social service professionals serving Chicago's Deaf community. The group met regularly throughout the year and many of its members were Deaf themselves. The educator reported that their response was very positive both to the having such a prevention education presentation available to their clients and to the presentation itself. The professionals who attended that presentation were considered consultants and were not included in the data described in this paper. They were encouraged to help market the presentation to their clients.

The educator incorporated participatory activities into the presentation not only to increase interest and reduce anxiety about the topic, but also to support comprehension of some very complex concepts. An introductory "game" that at first glance appeared to simply be an ice breaker involved asking participants to form a circle and follow three rules: (1) After a ball is first thrown to you, randomly throw it to someone who has not yet touched it and then maintain that toss pattern every time the ball begins a new cycle. (2) Do not allow any balls to fall to the ground. (3) If you drop a ball, you must step out of the circle and stop participating. After the first ball had completed a few successful cycles, the leader would add another ball to the game and then a third. It became increasingly difficult for the participants remaining in the circle to not allow the three balls to fall to the ground. The ultimate purpose of the game was to help demonstrate a complicated medical concept: how the infection-fighting T-cells inside our bodies become overwhelmed and unable to protect our bodies after the HIV virus has entered, multiplied and begun the process of destroying T-cells.

Published research in the area of HIV/AIDS prevention for the Deaf community is in its infancy. Two studies examined the HIV/AIDS knowledge of Deaf high school students; both studies reported large gaps in what the students understood about HIV/AIDS and how the disease is transmitted (Luckner & Gonzales, 1993; Baker-Duncan, et al., 1997). The health survey of 203 Deaf persons mentioned earlier in this paper suggested that Deaf adults also experience significant gaps in what they understand about HIV/AIDS. Almost one third of the respondents did not consider "not using a condom when having sex with someone you don't know" a risk factor for HIV/AIDS. Over 40% did not view "sharing needles when using IV drugs" as risky (Advocate Health Care & Sinai Health System, 2003). There were two published studies comparing the HIV/AIDS knowledge and/or attitudes of a group of Deaf persons to a group of hearing persons (Woodroffe, et al., 1998; Heuttel & Rothstein, 2001). Heuttell and

Rothstein's study compared Deaf and hearing college students and the other study compared a community-based group of Deaf adults to a demographically similar group of hearing adults. Both of these studies demonstrated the need to develop interventions that would help the Deaf community increase their knowledge of HIV/AIDS issues and, therefore, catch up to the hearing population. All four studies illustrated the need for increased knowledge of and healthier attitudes towards HIV/AIDS within the Deaf community. We, however, were unable to find any published articles that examined the impact that prevention interventions may have on the Deaf community. Because of the low incidence of deafness, the fact that Deaf persons are scattered throughout large geographic areas without the establishment of a Deaf neighborhood, and the stigma that HIV/AIDS continues to have within the Deaf community, it has been difficult to recruit the critical mass of participants necessary for formal statistical analyses. In this early study, however, we have attempted to move the research on HIV/AIDS prevention for the Deaf community to this next level of investigation.

Method

Participants

This study recruited adult members of the Deaf community from within Chicagoland's greater metropolitan area and from a mid-sized Midwestern city about 150 miles west of Chicago. Four different subgroups of the Deaf community voluntarily attended an HIV/AIDS prevention education presentation: a group of Deaf suburbanites the majority of whom were white (N=12), a group of city-based Deaf Latinos (N=20), a group of city-based Deaf African Americans (N=18) and a group of Deaf adults from the midsized Midwestern city the majority of whom were white (N=31). The presentations each were announced on Deaf Illinois News, a list serve established to announce important events of interest to the Deaf community, and through handouts and face-to-face announcements. All four subgroups were composed of people who had been meeting regularly for social purposes and the leaders of each of these social groups strongly supported the presentation and helped with recruitment. The marketing of the presentations emphasized the social aspect of attending as much as the educational benefit. Free food was provided and at the end of the presentation, attendees participated in a raffle for a $25 gift certificate to a neighborhood grocery store. Participants were allowed to remain on the premises after the presentation ended to promote socialization.

Procedure

Participants were asked to anonymously complete a pre- and post-knowledge and attitude survey. The surveys were printed in English for purposes of collecting the data but the presenter, one of three native signers formally trained in HIV/AIDS education, converted each question into ASL. The lead presenter attended all three presentations to assure consistency in the information provided. The survey included ten basic statements about HIV/AIDS and asked the respondent to answer by circling True, False, or Don't Know (see Table 1). The five attitude statements asked the respondent to answer by circling Agree Strongly, Agree Somewhat, Disagree Somewhat, Disagree Strongly (see Table 2). A second attached sheet of statements was completed after the slide show presentation and question/answer session. No identifying information was gathered except for recording in which group the survey had been completed.

Table 1: Questions from HIV/AIDS survey

1. AIDS means Acquired Immune Deficiency Syndrome.
2. AIDS and HIV are the same illness.
3. HIV affects the person before AIDS does.
4. AIDS can be transmitted to another person by drinking from the same glass, using the same toilet, or sharing food.
5. AIDS can be transmitted to another person through contact with infected blood or bodily fluids.
6. AIDS can be transmitted to another person through unprotected vaginal and oral sex.
7. Only homosexuals can get HIV and develop AIDS.
8. An infected person can pass the virus that can lead to AIDS even though that person isn't sick.
9. Most people who develop AIDS eventually get well.
10. AIDS weakens the body's ability to fight off disease.

Table 2: Attitude questions from HIV/AIDS survey

1. AIDS is a health scare I take very seriously.
2. I think it is important not to have sex before marriage.
3. I always try to use a condom during sex.
4. If my partner won't have safe sex, then I won't have sex with that person.
5. I would not have unprotected sex with an IV (intravenous) drug user.

Materials

The survey was copied, with permission, from the instrument developed by the researchers in the study mentioned above that had compared the HIV knowledge of a group of Deaf college students with a comparable group of hearing students (Heuttel & Rothstein, 2001). The researchers had adapted the knowledge and attitude questions from a study by Koopman, et.al. (1990) to better fit the linguistic needs of the Deaf community. The answers for the ten knowledge questions were converted to scores of "1" for correct answers and "0" for incorrect answers or a response of Don't know. Each respondent's knowledge questions were summed to create a Knowledge Index score. The answers for the five attitude questions were converted to "4" for Agree Strongly down to "1" for Disagree Strongly and analyzed individually. Agree Strongly responses were always the healthiest. If a respondent did not complete each question on both the pre and post-test, that answer was eliminated from the data.

Results

In order to compare the participants who did and did not change from pre- to post-test using Heuttel and Rothstein's measure, we created two groups for analyzing responses to each question. The first group (change) consisted of all the people who had answered the question incorrectly at time 1 (before we did our presentation); we predicted their level of knowledge would change and they would answer the question correctly at time 2 (after we did our presentation). The second group (no-change) consisted of people who had answered the question correctly at time 1; we predicted they would not change their status at time 2. We next compared the groups' percent correct for each question at time 2 predicting that if our presentation were successful, the people in the change group would have "caught up" in their knowledge of HIV/AIDS and would have the same percent correct as the no-change group. The results of these analyses are shown in Table 3.

Table 3: Dichotomous variables

	N		Percent Correct		Standard Error		CI Overlap?	Chi-square
	Change	No-Change	Change	No-Change	Change	No-Change		
Q1	31	42	79.5	92.9	14.2	7.8	No	3.1
Q2	42	22	73.7	91.7	13.3	11.5	No	3.3
Q3	32	41	91.4	89.1	9.7	9.5	No	0.1
Q4	44	33	93.6	97.1	7.2	5.7	No	0.5
Q5	29	51	99.0	98.1	3.6	3.7	No	0.5
Q6	26	49	92.9	92.5	9.9	7.4	No	0.9
Q7	34	35	73.9	99.9	14.8	1.0	Yes	10.7*
Q8	34	30	75.6	83.3	14.4	13.3	No	0.7
Q9	22	46	81.5	85.2	16.2	10.3	No	0.2
Q10	38	38	95.0	92.7	6.9	8.3	No	0.2

Note: * $p < .01$

Examining results for question 1 ("AIDS means Acquired Immune Deficiency Syndrome"), it can be seen that 31 participants answered the question incorrectly at time 1 and, therefore, were placed in the change group for question 1; 42 participants answered the question correctly at time 1 and, therefore, were placed in the no-change group. In other words, at time 1, 0% of the people in the change group had given a correct answer to question 1 and 100% of the people in the no-change group had given a correct answer to question 1. It appeared that the samples of people in the change and no-change groups at time 1 were each chosen from a different population; the change sample appeared to be chosen from a population of Deaf people who did not have the knowledge necessary to answer the question correctly and the no-change sample appeared to be chosen from a population of Deaf people who did have the knowledge necessary to answer the question correctly. At time 2 (after the presentation), 79.5% of the participants in the change group were able to answer question 1 correctly. The participants in the no-change group, who had 100% accuracy at time 1, answered the question correctly in 92.9% of the cases. This suggests that a small number of participants may have guessed and not really known the correct answer at time 1 and then guessed wrong at time 2.

Next, Standard Errors are presented. A standard error is a statistic that assumes that every sample we choose creates some bias in the results that occur. We did not test every Deaf person living in the Midwest. Our sample contained only a small number of the Midwestern Deaf population. The standard error helps us estimate what the range of percent correct scores for the change group and no-change group associated with each question would be if we were to test an unlimited amount of samples of Deaf people living in the Midwest. Subtracting and adding these standard errors to the percent correct statistic that occurred in our particular sample provides 95% confidence intervals for our percent correct statistics. That means we can be 95% confident that the true percent correct score for the population from which our sample was chosen lies somewhere within that range. For the change group on question one, the confidence interval for percentage answering correctly at time 2 is 65.3% to 93.7% (original percentage of 79.5% +/- a standard error of 14.2); the confidence interval for the no-change group is 85.1%–100% (92.9% +/- a standard error of 7.8). The next column indicates whether or not the confidence intervals for the change and no-change groups overlap. If the confidence intervals do overlap, then we cannot conclude that the sample of participants in the change group and the sample of participants in the no-change group continue to be drawn from two separate populations: a population of Deaf people who have enough information to answer correctly and a population of Deaf people who do not know enough to answer correctly. In other words, it suggests that the participants in the change group have caught up with the no-change group in the amount of knowledge they have about the question under study. If the confidence intervals of percent correct scores for each sample do *not* overlap, then we have evidence that the samples were drawn from different populations. This suggests that the participants in the change group have a significantly different (i.e., lower) level of knowledge than the no-change group and have *not* caught up in their understanding of the information presented in the question under study. A "yes" in this column indicates that we can conclude with a high level of confidence that at time 2 the participants in the change and no-change samples continue to be drawn from different populations in regard to their level of knowledge.

Comparing the two confidence intervals for question 1 reveals that they overlap by close to nine percentage points. Therefore, we cannot be certain that the two samples were drawn from different populations of respondents. This statistical data suggests that the participants in the change group knew as much about the information presented in question 1 as the no-change group after the presentation. In fact, the only item demonstrating non-overlap of confidence intervals was question 7 ("Only homosexuals can get HIV and develop AIDS"). Therefore, it appears that a participant's understanding of the information associated with this item may be harder to change among respondents who do not know the answer at time 1 than it was for the other questions. This is further supported by the Chi-square analyses in the final column of Table 2. A 2x2 Chi-square analysis yielded statistically significant differences ($p< .01$) for only this specific question, again suggesting that the percent correct across the post-test change and no-change groups is different.

We next compared scores on the attitude questionnaire from pre to post-test using paired-samples t-tests. The results of these analyses are presented in Table 4. Results indicate that each attitude changed significantly by moving towards a more health-promoting position from pre to post-test with the exception of attitude question 1 ("AIDS is a health scare I take very seriously").

Table 4: Pre–post independent samples t-test

| | N | Pre-test | | Post-test | | t |
		Mean	SD	Mean	SD	
Question 1	73	3.3	0.9	3.2	1.0	0.7
Question 2	73	2.7	0.9	3.2	1.0	4.1*
Question 3	74	2.9	1.1	3.4	1.0	3.5*
Question 4	74	2.9	0.9	3.6	0.8	5.1*
Question 5	74	3.2	0.8	3.7	0.7	4.7*

Note: * $p<.05$

Discussion

The current study attempted to examine whether an HIV/AIDS educational intervention could increase knowledge for a sample of diverse Deaf individuals from the community. This study represents the first attempt to demonstrate the benefits of such a program for this population.

The results indicated that our sample was able to benefit from the educational intervention. For each of the ten knowledge questions, we broke the sample into two sub-samples: those who did and did not answer the item correctly at pre-test. We determined that the group that did not answer the question correctly at pre-test would "change" and would have enough knowledge to be able to answer the question correctly after participating in our culturally sensitive presentation; we also determined that the group that did answer correctly at pre-test would remain constant (no-change) and would continue to answer correctly after the presentation. At post-test, there were no significant differences in how well the change and no-change groups correctly responded on nine of the ten knowledge questions. The only question in which the participants in the change group remained behind the no-change group in their ability to answer correctly was question 7 ("Only homosexuals can get HIV and develop AIDS").

We next compared our group on several pre- and post-test Likert scale items related to attitudes and behavior. Our sample showed statistically significant increases in healthy attitudes and behavior using a paired-samples t-test for attitude questions 2–5. This again suggests that the intervention improved awareness that may lead to healthier attitudes and safer sexual behavior among our Deaf population.

The N was small for this early investigation into the impact of using culturally sensitive HIV prevention education materials with Deaf persons who communicate using American Sign Language. The results, however, suggest that when Deaf persons are exposed to Deaf-friendly HIV prevention interventions, they can gain knowledge and develop healthier attitudes. This study did not assess whether the change in knowledge and attitudes continued past the day of the presentation. On knowledge question 7, however, the slide show intervention did not help the group of respondents who answered incorrectly at pre-test catch up in their level of knowledge to the group who knew the correct answers at pre-test.

Although the information assessed in question 7 ("Only homosexuals can get HIV and develop AIDS") was emphasized during the presentation, 26% of the 34 respondents who had answered this question incorrectly at the pre-test continued to do so after the slide show intervention. It appears that it requires more than one hour of prevention education to challenge the belief that HIV/AIDS is only a gay man's disease.

Despite this reluctance among some participants to accept HIV/AIDS as a disease that could affect anybody, overall, the participants demonstrated significant positive shifts in their post-test attitudes ($p<.05$) regarding the importance of protecting themselves from becoming infected with HIV in four out of five attitude questions (questions 2–5). The first attitude question (AIDS is a health scare I take very seriously) did not even change in the proposed positive direction. One possibility is that participants felt less anxious about AIDS at the end of the presentation because of their increased knowledge and their answers reflected the reduction in fear associated with their increased comprehension. Perhaps this question should be rewritten if the survey were to be used again in future research.

Finally, if this survey is utilized in other studies, it also is recommended that knowledge question 9 ("Most people who develop AIDS eventually get well") be modified to read, "Most people who develop AIDS eventually are cured." The question as it currently reads could be interpreted to mean that someone with AIDS will eventually feel better and be able to live a productive life which for many AIDS patients is now true.

From the perspective of a statistician, the number of Deaf community members who participated in this HIV prevention presentation is low; from the perspective of an educator or provider, however, 81 more Deaf people have been exposed to how to live a healthy life and how to share and discuss health concerns related to HIV/AIDS despite its stigma within the Deaf community. One participant commented on an evaluation sheet that one of the presentation's strengths was, "hearing from a Deaf man honest answers about HIV." The question is where to go from here.

This investigation went beyond examining HIV/AIDS knowledge in the Deaf community as it already exists and began exploring the level of change that can occur in a Deaf person's knowledge of and attitudes towards HIV/AIDS related issues following a Deaf-friendly intervention.

The ultimate goal of health care providers is to improve the Deaf community's access to health promotion information and, therefore, hopefully improve the chances that Deaf persons will practice healthy behaviors. Given the current emphasis on best practices, however, an equally important goal is to advance research in this area of study to the next level of investigation and compare the pre- and post-test knowledge and attitude scores of Deaf persons who have been randomly assigned to one of three groups – a control group that does not receive any type of HIV/AIDS information between times 1 and 2, a group that is exposed to English-based HIV/AIDS prevention education materials between times 1 and 2 and a group that is exposed to a Deaf-friendly presentation of that same HIV/AIDS prevention education information. This more sophisticated design is necessary to identify the use of linguistically and culturally sensitive HIV/AIDS health promotion materials (as opposed to English-based text materials) as a best practice when educating Deaf persons. Because of the difficulty in recruiting high numbers of Deaf persons, especially for HIV/AIDS related activities, this goal probably can occur only if the study can expand its scope beyond the limits of one local community.

The results of this study have suggested that culturally and linguistically sensitive HIV prevention education materials can have a positive impact on the Deaf community. The low incidence of Deafness, however, places serious limits on the funding available for designing and implementing these materials. The question then becomes, "What can community agencies across the country do to create cost efficient methods for educating the Deaf community about HIV/AIDS?" The answer is collaboration, cross-training, and technology.

Collaboration between two existing agencies helps to avoid the expense of start-up costs. An ideal collaboration would be between an established HIV/AIDS program for the hearing community with a social service agency whose staff have specialized competencies in American Sign Language and Deaf culture. Together, through cross-training and cross-referrals, they can better meet the prevention education and treatment needs of the Deaf community. Cross-training between agencies is a professional form of bartering that can improve the quality of care provided at both sites for a minimal cost.

Finally, technology can help to duplicate and disperse resources in a low-cost manner. For example, the script of the slide show described in this paper has been rewritten to better fit the format of a video. This video, "Ignore AIDS? CAN'T!", includes the same information as the slide show but presents the information in three different formats: (1) a story-based presentation in which Deaf actors play Deaf characters whose lives are impacted by HIV/AIDS; (2) a narrated presentation which breaks into the story line to repeat and summarize important facts revealed throughout the story; (3) animated, graphic-based presentations which demonstrate the more complex, medically based concepts of the video (e.g., viral load and how medication works). Not only does having the information on a video help to standardize the presentation but it also creates a more efficient way of dispensing the information throughout the nation. Because of a public-private collaboration between the Illinois Department of Public Health and our Deaf and Hard of Hearing Program, we have been able to place this important video resource and additional ASL video clips on other STDs on the internet at www.advocatehealth.com/deaf. The web site appears to have been received very well by the Deaf community. The web site went live on October 12, 2005. During the last three months of 2005, there were 1,472 hits with 769 unique visitors. 57 visitors completed the web site's satisfaction survey; it is a 4-point Likert scale in American Sign Language. The six survey questions assess the user's satisfaction with the utility, clarity and quality of the information and with the clarity and quality of the signing. It also assesses the user's overall satisfaction with the web site and motivation to recommend the web site to friends. For example, when asked to what extent the information will help the user make decisions about HIV/AIDS and other STDs in the future, the choices range from "often" (4 points) to "sometimes" (3 points), "rarely" (2 points) and "never" (1 point). The mean score for that question is 3.77. When the user is asked if he or she would recommend the web site to friends with choices ranging from "definitely will" (4 points) to "probably will" (3 points), "probably will not" (2 points) and "definitely will not" (1 point), the mean score is 3.92.

Teleconferencing can also connect experts in HIV/AIDS prevention education for the Deaf community to culturally competent agencies in need of HIV/AIDS training and to HIV/AIDS clinics in need of sensitization towards Deaf culture issues. The halls of a culturally and linguistically sensitive and accessible HIV/AIDS "neighborhood" clinic for the members of America's Deaf community can most efficiently be created not through concrete and lumber but through the computer and teleconferencing cables of technology. Recognizing the important role that technology can play in disseminating these materials, however, should not overshadow the importance of community involvement when utilizing the materials. Community involvement plays an important role in HIV/AIDS prevention education at two levels. The first level of involvement is a more abstract sense of community presence experienced by Deaf persons when they view the signed material. We have attempted to achieve this through the use of Deaf actors and by utilizing Deaf consultants at the different stages of script and video production. The second level involves a more direct, concrete community presence. The majority of Deaf sign language users who participated in focus groups in New York stated that they preferred HIV/AIDS information be disseminated by signing educators in small groups (Bat-Chava, et al., 2005). Based on this model, the standardized materials can be transported at low or no cost through technology and then taught to and supported by local peer educators.

Conclusion

This study suggests that a culturally and linguistically sensitive presentation of HIV/AIDS prevention education materials can significantly increase a Deaf person's level of knowledge and can significantly strengthen a Deaf person's attitudes towards proactively reducing one's risk of becoming infected with HIV. This information is applicable to both researchers and community members. It is hoped that researchers will continue to refine the design and subsequently examine the efficacy of culturally sensitive HIV/AIDS prevention education materials for Deaf communities locally, nationally and internationally. The modification of the face-to-face slideshow prevention education materials used in this study into the more portable and standardized format of a videotape presentation increases the likelihood that this study could be replicated across Deaf communities that communicate in American Sign Language. The cost to convert the videotape (which has English subtitles) into other sign languages would be prohibitive but the video could be used to train native signers from other countries (with the support of multilingual sign language interpreters) so that they could develop their own scripted face-to-face presentations. This linguistically modified version of the materials could then be used to internationally replicate the Chicago-based study described in this paper in a more cost-efficient manner. Until that occurs, however, one can only begin to speculate about the applicability of this local study to a larger international audience.

Three variables, however, support the speculation that this local study could apply to expanded audiences. Firstly, the results of this study on a Deaf population reflect the conclusion supported by multiple assessments of health communication strategies conducted among multi-cultural hearing populations: culturally and linguistically sensitive communication is a necessary component towards improving health knowledge and health practices. This topic is of such a high priority among hearing populations that a Health Communication Focus Area has been included in the U.S. Department of Health and Human Services publication of *Healthy people 2010* (U.S. Department of Health and Human Services, 2000). Secondly, although the demographics of the participants in this study were not formally analyzed, it has been suggested that the local pool from which they were recruited reflects a diverse range of ethnic/racial, educational and socioeconomic backgrounds (Margellos-Anasat, et al., 2005). Thirdly, as described earlier in this paper, there is a common belief among researchers in the field of Deafness and health that a majority of Deaf adults share several common experiences in trying to access health information and health care services. It would not be that large of a leap to conclude, therefore, that these common barriers to accessible health knowledge and treatment could be reduced with exposure to common interventions. Ideally, however, one would hope that future research will replicate and refine the methodology and design of this study within multiple settings to help reach more definitive conclusions on the efficacy of culturally and linguistically sensitive HIV/AIDS prevention education materials among national and international Deaf communities.

The results of this study challenge researchers to move towards developing best practices for providing HIV/AIDS education to the Deaf community. The results, however, also challenge community members to utilize the best practices suggested by researchers. Community members are challenged to use the free materials described in this paper to help train peer educators who then can use the materials to educate the members of their local communities about HIV/AIDS and STDs. Deaf peer educators can play an important role in fighting the AIDS epidemic at all stages: educating their communities on how to lower their risk of becoming infected, encouraging their community to get tested, and supporting those community members who already have become infected with HIV/AIDS and/or STDs to seek early care and comply with treatment recommendations. Many Deaf persons grow up in environments that encourage them to depend on hearing people to navigate, communicate and make decisions for them within health care environments; the results of this study encourage members of the Deaf community to take a more proactive approach to their health.

References

Adams, J. W. (1997). *You and your deaf child*. Washington, D.C.: Gallaudet University Press.

Advocate Health Care, & Sinai Health Systems. (2004). *Improving access to health and mental health for Chicago's Deaf community: A survey of Deaf adults (final survey report)*. Retrieved March 1, 2004, from

Baker-Duncan, N., Dancer, J., Detholyn, G., Highly, P., & Gibson, B. (1997). Deaf adolescents' knowledge of AIDS. *American Annals of the Deaf, 142 (5)*, 268–272.

Barnett, S. (1999). Clinical and cultural issues in caring for deaf people. *Family Medicine, 31 (1)*, 17–22.

Bat-Chava, Y., Martin, D., & Kosciw, J. G. (2005). Barriers to HIV/AIDS knowledge and prevention among deaf and hard of hearing people. *AIDS Care, 17 (5)*, 623–634.

Ebert, D. A., & Heckerling, P. S. (1995). Communication with deaf patients: Knowledge, beliefs, and practices of physicians. *Journal of the American Medical Association, 273 (3)*, 227–229.

Gaskins, S. (1999). Special population: HIV/AIDS among the deaf and hard of hearing. *Journal of the Association of Nurses in AIDS Care, 10 (2)*, 75–78.

Guthmann, D., & Blozis, A. (2001). Unique issues faced by Deaf individuals entering substance abuse treatment and following discharge. *American Annals of the Deaf, 146 (3)*, 294–304.

Health Resources, & Services Administration/HIV AIDS Bureau. (2001). *HRSA care action: HIV/AIDS in the deaf and hard of hearing.* Rockville, MD.

Heuttel, K. L., & Rothstein, W. G. (2001). HIV/AIDS knowledge and information sources among Deaf and hearing college students. *American Annals of the Deaf, 146 (3)*, 280–286.

Koopman C., Rotheram-Borus, M., Henderson, R, Bradley, J., & Hunter, I. (1990) Assessment of knowledge of AIDS and beliefs about AIDS prevention among adolescents. *AIDS Education and Prevention, 2*, 58–70.

Luckner, J. L., & Gonzales, B. R. (1993). What deaf and hard-of-hearing adolescents know and think about AIDS. *American Annals of the Deaf, 138 (4)*, 338–342.

Mallinson, R. K. (2004a). Perceptions of HIV/AIDS by deaf gay men. *Journal of the Association of Nurses in AIDS Care, 15 (4)*, 27–36.

Mallinson, R. K. (2004b). Deaf culture: When "positive" is a good thing. *Journal of the Association of Nurses in AIDS Care, 15 (4)*, 21–22.

Margellos-Anast, H., Hedding, T., Perlman, T., Miller, L., Rodgers, R., Kivland, L., DeGutis, Dorothea, Giloth, B., & Whitman, S. (2005). Developing a standardized comprehensive health survey for use with deaf adults. *American Annals of the Deaf, 150 (4)*, 388-396.

McEwen, E., & Anton-Culver, H. (1988). The medical communication of Deaf patients. *The Journal of Family Practice, 26 (3)*, 289–291.

Mitchell, R. E. (2005). *Can you tell me how many deaf people there are in the United States?* Gallaudet Research Institute, Gallaudet University, Washington, D.C. Retrieved March 20, 2005, from http://gri.gallaudet.edu/Demographics/deaf-US.html

Mitchell, R. E., Young, T. A., Bachleda, B., & Karchmer, M. A. (2006). How many people use ASL in the United States? Why estimates need updating. *Sign Language Studies, 6 (3).* (accepted for publication; for a draft go to: gri.gallaudet.edu)

Munro-Ludders, B. (2001, August 1). Personal communication to Toby Perlman by the Statewide Coordinator of Deaf and Hard of Hearing Services, Illinois Office of Mental Health.

Neisser, A. (1990). *The other side of silence: Sign language and the Deaf community in America.* Washington, D.C.: Gallaudet University Press.

Peinkoffer, J. R. (1994). HIV education for the Deaf, a vulnerable minority. *Public Health Reports, 109 (3),* 390–396.

Phillips B. A. (1996). Bringing culture to the forefront: formulating diagnostic impressions of Deaf and hard of hearing people at times of medical crisis. *Professional Psychology: Research and Practice, 27 (2),* 137–144.

Pollard, R. Q. (1998). Psychopathology. In M. Marschark & D. Clark (Eds.), *Psychological perspectives on Deafness. Vol. 2.* Mahwah, NJ: Lawrence Erlbaum. 171–197.

Rudd, R. (2003), Improvement of health literacy. In U.S. Department of Health and Human Services, *Communicating health: Priorities and strategies for progress.* Washington, D.C.: USDHHS, Office of Disease Prevention and Health Promotion. 35–60.

Schein, J. D., & Delk, M. T. (1974). *The deaf population of the United States.* Silver Spring, MD: National Association of the Deaf.

Steinberg, A. G., Wiggins, E. A., Barmada, C. H., & Sullivan, V. J. (2002). Deaf women: Experiences and perceptions of healthcare system access. *Journal of Women's Health, 11 (8),* 729–741.

U.S. Department of Health and Human Services. (2000). *Healthy people 2010* (2nd ed.). Washington, D.C.: U.S. Government Printing Office.

Witte, T. N., & Kuzel, A. J. (2000). Elderly deaf patients' health care experiences. *Journal of the American Board of Family Practice, 13 (1),* 17–22.

Woodroffe T., Gorenflo D. W., & Meador H. E. (1998). Knowledge and attitudes about AIDS among Deaf and hard of hearing persons. *AIDS Care, 10 (3),* 377–386.

Contact information
Toby S. Perlman, Ph.D.

Advocate Illinois Masonic Behavioral Health Services
Chicago, Illinois
938 West Nelson – Third Floor
Chicago, IL 60657
email: Toby.Perlman@advocatehealth.com
Scott C. Leon, Ph.D.
Loyola University Chicago
Department of Psychology
Chicago, IL

An HIV knowledge and attitude survey of deaf U.S. adults

Marjorie F. Goldstein, Elizabeth Eckhardt, Patrice Joyner and Roberta Berry

Deaf Worlds
2006 | vol 22 (1)
Forest Books ©
ISSN 1362–3125

Key words

HIV/AIDS, deafness, survey methodology, American Sign Language, HIV knowledge, HIV attitudes

Abstract

There are few data-based studies about deaf persons' HIV knowledge and attitudes. In part, this is because of the difficulties in administering large-scale surveys to deaf individuals in sign language. This study surveyed 452 deaf adults in eight U.S. states about their HIV knowledge and attitudes in American Sign Language (ASL) via laptop computer. Results showed that while most participants had basic HIV knowledge, there were gaps in knowledge about transmission and protection. The mean knowledge score on a seven-item scale was 4.6 (s.d., 2.28). In addition, 23% of participants answered 'yes' to the statement: 'HIV is a hearing person's disease'. These participants were also more likely to say that they would not work with a person who had AIDS and that getting HIV is a person's own fault. These findings indicate that more accessible HIV education and prevention programs are needed in the U.S. deaf population.

Biographies

Marjorie F. Goldstein, Ph.D., is a principal investigator at Social Sciences Innovations Corporation and National Development and Research Institutes, Inc. where she has conducted survey research for deaf individuals in several health areas. Other areas of interest include substance abuse, and prevention and treatment for persons who are HIV positive.

Elizabeth A. Eckhardt, Ph.D., is project director of Deaf Research at National Development and Research Institutes, Inc. Previous related research has included the development of surveys in ASL to study substance use, tobacco use, mental health, and HIV. Currently she is completing her dissertation which analyzes in depth interviews with deaf adults conducted in ASL to study HIV related health behaviors. Eckhardt is in the doctoral program in clinical Social Work at New York University.

Patrice Joyner, M.S.W., is assistant project director of Deaf Research at National Development and Research Institutes, Inc. Previous related research has included the development of surveys in ASL to study HIV/AIDS knowledge among the deaf adults. She has participated in all aspects of the translation procedure for the project. Joyner is deaf and has extensive experience providing case management and mental health services to individuals who are deaf. She has acted as a consultant for all previous research and has participated on translation teams, facilitated focus groups and acted as a sign model for the PSE version of substance use and tobacco related questionnaires.

Roberta Berry, M.F.A., is a Senior Research Assistant at National Development Research Institutes, Inc. She helped to develop and administer the HIV Knowledge Survey of Deaf Adults and also was a member of the English to ASL translation team. In 2005, Berry graduated from an ASL interpreter training program.

Introduction
While HIV incidence has been declining overall, in the United States, its prevalence has been increasing, in part due to the better treatments that have been available since 1996. The HIV incidence, prevalence, prevention needs, and risk behavior of deaf individuals have rarely been systematically studied and therefore remain largely unknown.

Barriers to acquisition of health information by deaf persons
It has been estimated that deaf persons are up to eight years behind the general public in their knowledge of disease prevention (Bares, 1992; Doyle, 1995; HRSA, 2001).[1] Classrooms and formal information techniques are not the most common avenue for acquiring information for this population (Kennedy & Bucholz, 1995). Much information reaches deaf individuals through the "deaf grapevine". The deaf grapevine is a social network/affiliate system of deaf persons that crosses geographic boundaries. Historically, this "grapevine" has enabled deaf persons to share crucial information. One problem with this informal mode of acquiring information is that myths and misinformation may be construed as truth and passed on to others (Peinkofer, 1994; Joseph et al., 1995; Kennedy & Bucholz, 1995; Gaskins, 1999; Heuttel & Rothstein, 2001). As a relatively "new" disease, most knowledge of HIV/AIDS, from categorizing it as a syndrome, through the discovery of the virus that causes it, to the development of effective treatments, has occurred within the past 20 years. Thus, there has been little time for the deaf community to develop strategies for dealing with this particular disease, making the task of bringing preventive messages about HIV/AIDS to individuals who are deaf exceedingly difficult. In addition, since HIV is principally acquired though private (sexual) or illegal (drug use) behaviors, it is highly stigmatized. Thus for deaf individuals who are already members of a minority group that experiences discrimination and is often stigmatized, it is particularly difficult to acknowledge the presence of a stigmatizing condition such as HIV/AIDS. For example, it has been found that young adults who are deaf reported that they were reluctant to get HIV testing for fear of others finding out (Silvestre et al., 2002).

HIV/AIDS prevention efforts within the general U.S. (hearing) population have primarily utilized television, radio programs, print media, and lectures as means of disseminating HIV/AIDS information. These means of communication are often unavailable or not readily available to individuals who are deaf because of low English literacy levels, the need for simplified captions, and/or the need for sign language interpretation (Kennedy & Bucholz, 1995; Gordon, Stump & Glaser, 1996). While efforts have been made to reach deaf people through captioned videos or television programs, and interpreted lectures, these may not be suitable for many deaf individuals since they require greater English reading proficiency or entry knowledge level than many deaf persons possess (Gaskins, 1999).

HIV risk

Several articles in the literature have suggested that deaf persons are at a higher risk of acquiring HIV than hearing persons (Bares, 1992; Peinkofer, 1994; Kennedy & Buchholz, 1995; Gaskins, 1999); however none of these provided prevalence rates. A search of unpublished sources located only one reliable U.S. data source regarding HIV among deaf persons. The Maryland Department of Health and Mental Hygiene began keeping data on hearing status (i.e., hearing vs. deaf or hard of hearing) at its Confidential HIV Testing, Counseling and Referral (CTR) sites beginning in 1997. In 2003, 2% of the more than 39,000 persons tested at CTR sites in the state of Maryland reported being deaf or hard of hearing. Of those, 4% tested HIV positive. The HIV positive rate among the hearing population was 2% (AIDS Administration, Maryland Department of Health and Mental Hygiene, unpublished). Leila Monaghan (this volume), working from general population statistics, uses these figures from Maryland to argue that the HIV positive rate of deaf people is between two and ten times higher than that of the hearing population. There is little information on HIV knowledge and risk behavior in U.S. deaf populations. In a 2001 survey by the Miami-Dade County Health Department (Florida), Office of HIV/AIDS Services, of 279 deaf and hard of hearing individuals, only 54% of the respondents gave the correct answer to the question, 'What is HIV?' (a virus/germ) and 60% could not identify 'HIV positive' as meaning that an individual was infected with HIV (Ullah & Moreno, 2001).

The are only a few studies of deaf persons' HIV risk behavior on the two major risk categories for HIV/AIDS in the U.S., injection drug use and men having sex with men. Lipton and Goldstein (1997) reported that rates of drug use among a sample of 825 deaf persons to be similar to those of hearing persons. In this study 11% deaf individuals who had tried to quit or cut down on drug use did not seek treatment because they thought that treatment program staff could not communicate with them, and 16% of those seeking treatment reported having been turned down because they were deaf.

Some investigators have noted that when gay deaf men form relationships or liaisons with hearing men, often the hearing lover is not familiar with sign language (Langholtz & Egbert-Rendon, 1991; Peinkofer, 1994; see also Dagron et al., 1998; Reeves, 1999). This means the likelihood of adequate HIV/AIDS related communication is decreased (Greenfield, 2003). The prevalence of these liaisons is unknown. Data from a 1999 survey of gay deaf men co-sponsored by Gay Men Fighting AIDS, and the British Deaf Association indicated that rates of unsafe sex in the past year were greater than those found in hearing samples of gay male hearing respondents in the other surveys. In this study, deaf men were also more likely than hearing men to endorse ineffective safe sex strategies (Reeves, 1999).

The study described in the present report sought to address the gaps in information about U.S. deaf persons' knowledge of and attitudes towards HIV. Because quantitative data are currently lacking, the method chosen was a survey of deaf individuals using a computerized, self-administered survey instrument in American Sign Language (ASL) with English captioning. Reported here are results related to HIV knowledge, attitudes, stigma, and sources of HIV information from the 452 study participants surveyed in eight U.S. states.

Methods
Instrument development
Several problems have emerged in efforts to survey deaf individuals:

a. Low English literacy among many profoundly and prelingually deaf persons makes it difficult to survey them with a written questionnaire. The average reading level for a deaf person graduating from high schools for the deaf in the U.S. is fourth grade (Steinberg, Sullivan & Leow, 1998).

b. Direct interviewing by non-signing professionals is not possible in the absence of an interpreter. If direct interview in spoken English is used, it is usually not possible for most deaf individuals to understand precisely what is being asked since, on average, the deaf adult will not understand more than 26%–40% of one-to-one conversation through lip-reading (Waldstein & Boothroyd, 1995).

c. Confidentiality is an issue when using an interpreter, especially when the subject matter is sensitive. Deaf individuals have expressed concern about the possible loss of privacy of personal information and have been reluctant to reveal information in an interview setting when an interpreter is present (MacDougall, 1991; Steinberg et al., 1998). In many communities this problem is magnified when the individual who is deaf anticipates future contact with the interpreter in other settings, making a sense of true privacy unattainable.

d. Even if surveys or questionnaires are administered one-on-one in ASL, there is no standardization of the actual sign translation. There is no standard written format for ASL (Woodroffe et al., 1998). Therefore each signer administering a questionnaire is likely to translate the same English sentence somewhat differently.

e. Using standardized measures developed for the general hearing population to assess individuals who are deaf may lead to problems with item validity. When using standardized measures with the deaf population, it is critical to ensure that each question is translated in such a way that it is culturally and linguistically accurate while still maintaining its original intent.

f. While ASL is the most commonly used manual language in the U.S., not all users have the same level of proficiency. Although ASL may be the language in which they communicate best, some deaf persons use a form of ASL that is a combination of simple signs and natural gestures to communicate. Preliminary qualitative work on this project consisted of focus groups of deaf individuals, at which questions to be used in the survey were presented in ASL. Participants were asked how they understood the ASL questions (e.g. 'did you understand the signs?').

Some groups incorporated strategies such as stories and gestures to explain concepts in the questions. Deaf professionals sometimes describe this type of ASL as highly contextualized since abstractions are explained via stories or examples. In order to make the HIV survey as accessible as possible and to include deaf persons who use this communication style, the survey was developed in two versions of ASL referred to as "full ASL" and "highly contextualized ASL" (HC).

Item selection

The full ASL version of the HIV survey contained 135 questions and the highly contextualized version contained 48 questions, a subset of the original 135. All items were chosen from items used in (1) in the National Health Interview Survey (Carey et al., 1997; CDC, 1999), (2) a written questionnaire for a deaf sample (Woodroffe et al., 1998), (3) a written survey with visual aids and signing assistance for a deaf sample (Ullah & Moreno, 2001), and (4) a survey used with specialized non-deaf populations (Wexler, 1997). An HIV survey script was developed with the written English version of each item.

Translation procedure

Generally accepted guidelines for translating research questions between two languages (Brauer, 1993; Edwards, 1994; Phillips, Hernandez & Ardon, 1994) were incorporated into the procedure used to translate the HIV survey script from written English into ASL. Among the techniques used, three are cited for attaining translation equivalence: back-translating, decentering, and a translation team approach (Edwards, 1994; Philips, Hernandez & Ardon, 1994).

The translation team for this project was comprised of three members, including two of us (Patrice Joyner and Roberta Berry). Joyner is a deaf social worker with extensive research and translation experience. Berry is fluent in ASL and has extensive experience working with a cross section of deaf adults with various levels of ASL skills. The third member of the translation team was a deaf HIV Health Educator, activist and advocate who has extensive experience educating the deaf community about HIV/AIDS.

The translation team reviewed the HIV survey script to discuss and agree upon the content and intent of each question. The team then explored various ASL translations in an attempt to maintain the content and intent while ensuring cultural and linguistic accuracy. One member of the team was videotaped signing these ASL versions. These videotaped translations were sent to the back translator and expert ASL reviewer. The back translator for this study is bilingual (English/ASL) and unfamiliar with the survey items. The expert reviewer is a deaf professional whose native language is ASL.

After review of back translations and expert comments, a final videotaped ASL version of the survey was sent to sign models to practice items from their assigned sections of the script. Each sign model was instructed to familiarize themselves with the translations exactly as they were on the videotape. Sign models were chosen for the clarity of their signing ability and represented diverse ethnic groups. These individuals (three male, three female) were all deaf and had previous experience as actors/actresses or other on-screen experience. Those who signed the HC questions had previous experience communicating with deaf persons who use this style of ASL.

Digital video editing and finishing process
Upon completion of the digital videotaping process, a multimedia company transferred digital video clips to the hard drives of six laptop computers. The multi-media company also programmed the survey, including skip instructions and functionality. The screen design was designed to be user friendly and provided the participant with the following function buttons: <u>See Again</u> which allows the participant to see the current question again; <u>Closed Captioning (CC)</u> which allows the participate to view the items in ASL alone or with English captions throughout the survey; and <u>Text Only</u> which allows participants to turn off the signing and view the survey in English text only. See Figure 1 for an illustration of a screen of the survey as it appears on laptop.

Figure 1: Survey screen

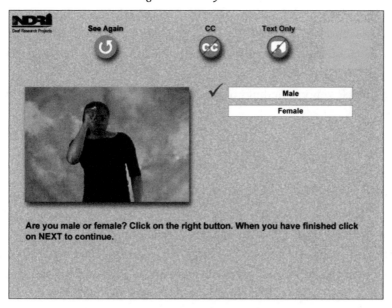

Participant recruitment and data collection

Criteria for inclusion were being deaf and over 18 years of age. The Institutional Review Board of National Development and Research Institutes, Inc. approved an exemption from written informed consent for this project because it is a completely anonymous survey and no identifying information is being collected. The survey was conducted in many locations including deaf fairs and 'expos', deaf adult education programs, deaf conferences, deaf alumni associations and deaf service organizations. Two recruitment strategies were used: at deaf fairs and 'expos' the study has its own table or booth to which participants are invited; at deaf service organizations, members or clients were invited to the organization's office during one or two designated days on which the survey staff is available to conduct surveys. The choice of survey version was made on an individual basis by the project staff member and the participant. Project staff members conversed briefly with each survey participant during the recruitment process. These conversations were a guide as to the appropriate survey version for each participant. When there was a question as to the appropriate version, the two versions were described to the participant who then made the choice. Participants were offered an incentive ($10 or a video tape rental gift card) for their participation. Survey participants were recruited from the states of New York, New Jersey, Colorado, California, Maryland, Pennsylvania, Michigan and Massachusetts, representing six regions of the United States. Time for completion of the survey was between 25 minutes and 1 hour and 15 minutes.

This article reports findings of the 452 deaf adults who participated in the survey.

Results
Data analysis
As a first step in the analysis, the data from the two versions of the survey were merged. Identical questions were asked on the two versions regarding demographics, deaf identity, attitudes, schooling, and sources of HIV information. A subset of HIV knowledge questions from the full version were asked on the HC version. Results on demographics, deaf identity and attitudes, and knowledge questions will be presented in this report.

The sample (n=452) was 56% female and 44% male and the mean age was 40 (range 18–93). With respect to ethnicity, 33% are of a Latino background. With respect to race, 30% identify as African American, 42% identify as White, 7% as Asian American, and 2% as Native American/Pacific Islander, and 19% as Other (75% of whom also self identify as Latino). Thirty-eight percent of the sample report that they are married or living as married, 43% were single/never married, and 19% report being divorced, separated or widowed. Sixty-nine percent report having completing twelfth grade or having education beyond high school graduation. Fifty-eight percent of the sample took the full ASL version and 42% took the highly contextualized (HC) version.

Eighty-one percent of the sample identified themselves as deaf while 19% identified as hard of hearing. With regard to their past educational experiences, 50% of the sample attended deaf schools, 15% attended hearing schools, and 23% attended both deaf and hearing schools. Data on type of school was missing or 'no school attendance' was indicated for the remaining 12%. When given a list of sources of HIV information, 55% indicated that they had received HIV information from friends, 50% from doctors, 35% from family members, 60% from school or training programs, and 77% from print or captioned media. Ten percent did not endorse any of the sources of HIV information.

The following variables were examined to assess whether or not they were related to the HIV knowledge scale score: gender, age, ethnicity, level of formal education, type of school (deaf school/hearing school/both), deaf identity (deaf/hard of hearing), sources of HIV information (among friends, family, doctors, school, and media), know (of) a deaf person who has HIV, and version of survey taken (regular ASL or HC). Of these variables, nine were significantly related to the knowledge score in bivariate analyses (where each variable was examined separately in relation to HIV knowledge scale score).

Table 1: Knowledge questions: Percent of correct response

Question	% correct
1. Can a pregnant woman who has HIV pass it on to her newborn baby?	59%
2. Can a man give HIV to a woman if they are having sex without a condom?	70%
3. Can a woman give HIV to a man if they are having sex without a condom?	67%
4. Can I get HIV from kissing someone on the cheek if that person is infected with HIV?	76%
5. Can a person get HIV from sharing a needle with a drug user who has HIV?	75%
6. Can a man who has HIV look well and healthy?	57%
7. AIDS is caused by a virus (kind of germ) called HIV?	62%

A subset of eight HIV knowledge questions from the full version were asked on the HC version. One item 'Can I get HIV from mosquitoes?' was not highly correlated with the others and was therefore not included in the scale. The other seven HIV knowledge items formed a highly reliable HIV knowledge scale (Cronbach's alpha = .82) (see Table 1). A knowledge scale score was then calculated by summing the number of correct answers to each of seven items. Next, participant characteristics (see Table 2) were examined using t-tests to determine if each had a statistically significant association with the HIV knowledge scale score. (Age, a continuous characteristic, was evaluated via a correlation coefficient.)

Table 2: Bivariate relationships of participant characteristics to knowledge scale score
n=452, mean score=4.6, s.d.=2.28, range=0–7

Characteristic	Mean Score	P Value
Gender		
Male	4.37	
Female	4.80	.05
Age	na	NS
Ethnicity		
White	5.13	.0001
Black	3.93	NS
Hispanic	4.52	.0001
Education		
Pre-secondary	3.60	
Post-secondary	5.06	.0001
Hearing school (some or all)	5.25	.0001
Deaf school only	4.33	.0001
Identity		
Deaf	4.57	
Hard of hearing	4.76	NS
Know (of) a deaf person with HIV		
Yes	5.36	
No	3.60	.0001
Any source of HIV information		
Yes	4.91	
No	2.27	.0001
Version of survey		
Full ASL	5.80	
HC ASL	3.28	.0001

We also asked the question: 'Can deaf people get HIV?' to which 33% of participants answered 'no' or 'don't know'. This item was not included in the scale since it was not taken from a scale used with the general population.

Next, a multivariate regression model was constructed with HIV knowledge score as the outcome. All variables which were significant in the bivariate analyses presented in table one were initially included. Those which remained significant in the equation when all other variables were controlled were: attendance at a deaf school (lower score), knowing (of) a deaf person with HIV (higher score), ASL version of the interview (HC ASL, lower score), identifying any source of HIV information (higher score), see Table 3.

Table 3: Multivariate regression model: Outcome is HIV knowledge score

Variable	Beta	P value
Attended deaf school	-.9719	.0001
Any HIV information	1.3113	.0001
Version (HC)	-.9619	.0001
Know HIV positive person	.9574	,0001

This model accounted for 41% of the variance in HIV knowledge score in this sample.

We were also interested in exploring the responses to the question in the attitude section, 'HIV is a hearing person's disease'. (The responses to this question were unrelated to the knowledge item on whether deaf people could be infected with HIV.) Only data from participants who responded either 'yes' or 'no' to this question were analyzed. Those who responded 'don't know' were not included in the analysis, since it was impossible to determine whether they had no opinion on the matter, did not understand the question, or thought we were asking about a factual matter rather than for their opinion.

Responses to other questions and participant characteristics were then tested for their association with this question. For binary items such as gender, Chi-square tests were used. For continuous variables such as the

HIV knowledge scale score, t-tests were used. Among the characteristics and items tested, the following were associated (at $p < .05$) with saying 'yes' to 'HIV is a hearing person's disease': responding 'no' to 'I would refuse to work with someone who has AIDS'; responding 'no' to 'When people get HIV is their own fault'; having less than a post secondary education; having attended a deaf school for all or part of one's education; being of Hispanic or Black ethnicity and; having a lower score on the HIV knowledge scale. However, when all of these variables were included in a multiple logistic regression model, the demographic characteristics dropped out, and only knowledge score and the two attitudinal variables (saying one would not work with someone who had AIDS and saying getting HIV is a person's own fault) remained as significant in the model.

Conclusion

This is the first large-scale survey ever conducted about HIV knowledge among deaf adults. While the sample is large (n=452), participants could not be randomly selected for inclusion. Random selection of deaf persons is not currently feasible in the United States, since there are no lists of deaf individuals from which to sample. In this study we were interested in persons who are affiliated with the deaf community and who use ASL as their main or preferred communication modality. In addition, since this was a structured anonymous survey, there was no opportunity for individuals to explain 'don't know' responses. Therefore, these responses were not included in some analyses. We did not attempt to compare results of responses on this survey to those in the general population due to the way our sample was assembled and because the items of greatest interest in this study (i.e. knowledge about HIV) have not been included in general population surveys for over five years.

Nevertheless, this study has many strengths including the accessibility afforded by questions available in two levels of ASL as well as captions, the standardization of questions in ASL which is rarely achieved, and the reliability of the HIV knowledge scale. The large number of participants, the extensive geographic area covered, the wide range of ages and educational backgrounds, and the representation of diverse ethnic groups in the sample add to the confidence that individuals representing multiple facets of the deaf community participated.

Our findings indicate that, although the majority of the survey participants answered each knowledge item correctly, between 30–40% of the sample did not know the correct answers to each of the questions. This is of concern since it indicates that there are substantial knowledge gaps regarding HIV among the deaf participants in this survey. Lack of knowledge, furthermore, was found not to be random within the sample. HIV knowledge scale score was influenced by: ethnicity, having a source of HIV information, choice of ASL version (indicative of level of ASL proficiency), knowing (of) a deaf person who has HIV and type(s) of schools attended (deaf vs. hearing). These findings demonstrate that acquisition of HIV knowledge among deaf adults is influenced by demographic characteristics (e.g. ethnicity), earlier experiences (type of school, years of education), ASL language usage, exposure to HIV information, and personal knowledge of a deaf person who has HIV.

While some of these characteristics are not amenable to change, others offer great opportunity to reach deaf adults in the community. For example, media (including captioned television programs, and print media such as newspapers and magazines) was the most frequently cited source of HIV information (cited by 77%). Greater efforts could be made to place informational articles written at the appropriate reading level and accompanied by pictures and diagrams in deaf publications. More public service announcements and educational programs could be captioned or be made available in sign language versions. Medical visits present another opportunity for education. Sign language or captioned media could be made available in doctors' offices enhancing the chance that correct information would be received by the deaf patient either through an interpreter or in writing from the doctor. The higher levels of knowledge found among participants who had attended some years of mainstream (or 'hearing') schools as compared to those who had attended only deaf schools demonstrated that deaf schools are another venue where HIV education is particularly needed.

We were somewhat surprised that so many of the study participants (23%) agreed with the statement that 'HIV is a hearing person's disease'. Since response to this question was not associated with the knowledge item which asked whether deaf people could get HIV, it seems that the question of HIV being a hearing disease taps into another construct. It may be that some deaf people regard HIV as having a source outside of their own community, even though deaf people can become infected. This is analogous to members of the general public viewing HIV as a 'gay disease' even though they know that heterosexuals can also be infected. Another possibility is that this is a form of 'community denial'. After decades of discrimination, deaf culture has only recently been recognized as a distinct subculture by other Americans and deaf persons may not want to admit that a stigmatized medical condition also affects their community. This possibility is supported by the significant association found between this item and other items designed to measure stigma (e.g. 'I would refuse to work with someone who has AIDS'). If community denial were just a mistaken notion which provided some possible psychological benefits, it would be harmless. However, if deaf people believe that HIV can not or will not enter their community, then they are unlikely to take preventive measures to avoid becoming infected either though sexual or drug use behavior. The idea that HIV is a hearing person's disease may have serious consequences and must be addressed as part of any disease prevention effort in the deaf community. The deaf community has also had negative experiences with both the medical establishment and governmental agencies (Bat-Chava, 1994). Together with other forms of prejudice deaf people have been subject to, these experiences may also lead to a lack of trust and belief in HIV prevention messages.

In summary, the findings of this study suggest that the majority of deaf people have accurate information about HIV and AIDS, and believe that the members of the deaf community like other people, are susceptible to HIV. However, there are a substantial percentage of persons who are deaf who are not well informed about HIV and how it is transmitted. There is also a substantial group who feel that HIV is a hearing people's disease. Whether this comes from misinformation or from denial, in combination with inaccurate information about HIV in general, it can lead people to unknowingly putting themselves at risk for becoming infected by HIV. Preventing this is the task of both deaf and hearing professional working in the deaf community, deaf schools, and deaf media.

Notes

1. While a common convention (Dolnick 1993; Lane, Hoffmeister & Bahan 1996; Mindness, 1999) has been to use an uppercase "D" to refer to that subset of individuals who are deaf and view themselves part of the deaf community and embrace deaf culture and ASL as their primary language, we did not attempt to assess deaf community affiliation in this survey.

References

AIDS Initiative for Deaf Services Task Force Information. *AIDS Project Hartford*. Retrieved June 1, 2005 from http://www.aidsprojecthartford.org/deafaidsct.html

Bares, B. (1992) Facing AIDS: How prevalent is this deadly disease in the deaf population? *Hearing Health, 8,* 12–16.

Bat-Chava, Y. (1994). Group identification and self-esteem of Deaf adults. *Personality and Social Psychology Bulletin, 20 (5),* 494–502.

Brauer, B. A. (1993). Adequacy of a translation of the MMPI into American Sign Language for use with deaf individuals: Linguistic equivalency issues. *Rehabilitation Psychology, 38 (4),* 247–260.

Carey, M. P., Morrison-Beedy, D., & Johnson, B. T. (1996). The HIV-knowledge, questionnaire: Development and evaluation of a reliable, valid, and practical self-administered questionnaire. *AIDS and Behavior, 1 (1),* 61–74.

Centers for Disease Control and Prevention. (1999). *National health interview survey (NHIS).* Maryland: U.S. Department of Health and Human Services, National Center for Health Statistics.

Centers for Disease Control and Prevention website. Retrieved January 29, 2003 from http://www.cdc.gov

Dagron, J., Boussard, B. L., Bruneau, B. C., Galiffet, G. F., Blanchard, B. J., Gargoier, G.C. & Moncelle, M. B. (1998). Study of the deaf population using the testing site for HIV from October 1996 to December 1997, Hospital La Salpetriere, Paris. *International Conference on AIDS, 12,* 1125. (abstract no. 60677)

Deren, S., Oliver-Velez, D., Finlinson, A., Robles, R., Andia, J., Colon, H. M., Kang, S.-Y., & Shedlin, M. (2003). Integrating qualitative and quantitative methods: Comparing HIV- related risk behaviors among Puerto Rican drug users in Puerto Rico and New York. *Substance Use and Misuse, 38 (1)*, 1–24.

Dolnick, E. (1993, September). Deafness as culture. *The Atlantic Monthly*, 37-53.

Doyle, A. G. (1995). AIDS knowledge, attitudes and behaviors among deaf college students: A preliminary study. *Sexuality and Disability, 13 (2)*, 107–134.

Dushay, R., Singer, M., Weeks, M, Rohena, L., & Gruber, R. (2001). Lowering HIV risk among ethnic minority drug users: Comparing culturally relevant targeted intervention to a standard intervention. *Journal of Drug and Alcohol Abuse, 27*, 501–524.

Edwards, N. C. (1994). Translating written material for community health research: Guidelines to enhance the process. *Canadian Journal of Public Health, 85 (1)*, 67–70.

Fitz-Gerald, D., & Fitz-Gerald, M. (1998). A historical review of sexuality education and deafness: Where have we been this century. *Sexuality and Disability, 16 (4)*, 240–259.

Gaskins, S. (1999). Special population: HIV/AIDS among the Deaf and hard of hearing. *Journal of the Association of Nurses in AIDS Care, 10 (2)*, 75–78.

General information on HIV and AIDS. (n.d.). Retrieved September 21, 2004, from http://www.cdc.gov/hiv/general.htm

Gordon, R. P., Stump, K., & Glaser, B. A. (1996). Assessment of individuals with hearing impairments: Equity in testing procedures and accommodations. *Measurement and Evaluation in Counseling and Development, 29*, 111–118.

Greenfield, B. (2003, December). Deaf be proud. *Time Out New York, 429-430*.

Haffner, D. W., & de Mauro, D. (1991). *Winning the battle: Developing support for sexuality and HIV/AIDS education*. New York: Siecus.

Health Resources and Services Administration (HRSA). *HRSA action: HIV/AIDS in the deaf and hard of hearing.* Retrieved April 15, 2001 from ftp://ftp.hrsa.gov/hab/hrsa.401.pdf

Heuttel, K. L., & Rothstein, W. G. (2001). HIV/AIDS knowledge and information sources among deaf and hearing college students. *American Annals of the Deaf, 146 (3),* 280–286.

Jemmott, J. B., Jemmott, L. S., Fong, G. T., & McCaftree, K. (1999). Reducing HIV risk-associated behavior among Black and Hispanic/ Latina women. *American Psychologist, 43,* 949–957.

Joseph, J. M., Sawyer, R., & Desmond, S. (1995). Sexual knowledge, behavior and sources of information among deaf and hard of hearing college students. *American Annals of the Deaf, 140 (4),* 338–345.

Kennedy, S. G., & Buchholz, C. L. (1995). HIV and AIDS among the deaf. *Sexuality and Disability, 13 (2),* 111–119.

Lane, H. L., Hoffmeister, R., & Bahan, B. J. (1996). *A journey into the Deaf-world.* San Diego, CA: Dawn Sign Press.

Langholtz, D. L., & Egbert Rendon, M. (1991). The deaf gay/lesbian client: Some perspectives. *American Deafness and Rehabilitation Association, 25,* 31–34.

Lipton, D. S., & Goldstein, M. F. (1997). Measuring substance abuse among the deaf. *Journal of Drug Issues, 27 (4),* 733–754.

Lipton, D. S., Goldstein, M. F., Fahnbulleh, F. W., & Gertz, E. N. (1996). The interactive video-questionnaire: A new technology for interviewing deaf persons. *American Annals of the Deaf, 141 (5),* 370–378.

Luckner, J. L., & Gonzales, R. B. (1993). What deaf and hard-of-hearing adolescents know and think about AIDS. *American Annals of the Deaf, 19 (8),* 338–342.

MacDougall, J. C. (1991). Current issues in deafness: A psychological perspective. *Canadian Psychology, 32 (4),* 612–627.

Mindness, A. (1999). *Reading between the signs.* Yarmouth, Maine: Intercultural Press.

O'Donnell, L., Sandoval, A., Vornfett, R., & DeJong, W. (1994). Reducing AIDS and other STDs among inner city Hispanics: The use of qualitative research in the development of video-based patient education. *AIDS Education and Prevention, 6,* 140–153.

Ortiz-Torres, B., Serrano-Garcia, I., & Torres-Burgos, N. (2000). Subverting culture: Promoting HIV/AIDS prevention among Puerto Rican and Dominican women. *American Journal of Community Psychology, 28 (6),* 859–881.

Parker, R. (2001) Sexuality, culture, and power in HIV/AIDS research. *Annual Review of Anthropology, 30,* 163–179.

Peinkofer, J. R. (1994). HIV education for the deaf: A vulnerable minority. *Public Health Reports, 109 (3),* 390–396.

Phillips, L. R., Hernandez, I. L., & Torres de Ardon, E. (1994). Focus on psychometrics: Strategies for achieving cultural equivalence. *Research in Nursing and Health, 17,* 149–154.

Reeves, D. (1999, October). *Deaf gay men not getting the message. F***sheet, 52.* Retrieved April 19, 2004 from http://www.metromate.org.uk/fsheet/52/dgmng.phtml

Silvestre, A. J., Faber, J. F., Shankle, M. D., & Kopelman, J. P. (2002). A model for youth in health planning: HIV prevention in Pennsylvania. *Perspectives on Sexual and Reproductive Health, 34,* 2.

Steinberg, A., Lipton, D. S., Eckhardt, E. A., Goldstein, M. F., & Sullivan, V. J. (1998). The diagnostic interview schedule for deaf patients on interactive video: A preliminary investigation. *American Journal of Psychiatry, 155 (11),* 1603–1604.

Steinberg, A., Sullivan, V. J., & Leow, R. (1998), Cultural and linguistic barriers to mental health service access: The deaf consumers perspective. *American Journal of Psychiatry, 155 (7),* 982–984.

Ullah, E., & Moreno, A. *Stop the silence: Deaf and hard of hearing survey,* Miami, Florida, Retrieved April 21, 2001 from http://www.doh.wstate.fl.us/disease_ctrl/aids/index.html

Volk, J. E., & Koopman, C. (2001). Factors associated with condom use in Kenya: A test of the Health Belief Model. *AIDS Education and Prevention, 13 (6),* 495–508.

Waldstein, R. S., & Boothroyd, A. (1995). Speechreading supplemented by single-channel and multichannel tactile displays of voice fundamental frequency. *Journal of Speech and Hearing Research, 38,* 690–705.

Wexler, S. (1997). AIDS knowledge and educational preferences of at-risk runaway/homeless and incarcerated youth. *Children and Youth Services Review, 19 (8),* 667–681.

Wilson, B., & Miller, R. L. (2003) Examining strategies for culturally grounded HIV prevention: A review. *AIDS Education and Prevention, 15 (2),* 184–202.

Woodroffe, T., Gorenflo, D. W., Meador, H. E., & Zazove, P. (1998). Knowledge and attitudes about AIDS among deaf and hard of hearing persons. *AIDS Care, 10 (3),* 377–386.

Contact information

Marjorie F. Goldstein, Ph.D.
Principal Investigator
National Development Research Institute, Inc.
71 West 23rd Street, 8th Floor
New York, NY 10010
Tel: +1 212 845 4400
TTY: +1 212 845 4569
Fax: +1 917 438 0894
email: Goldstein@ndri.org

HIV/AIDS in the Brazilian Deaf community: A personal note

Norine Berenz

Deaf Worlds
2006 | vol 22 (1)
Forest Books ©
ISSN 1362–3125

Key words
HIV/AIDS, Deafness, Brazilian Deaf community, importance of HIV/AIDS education, attitudes to Gay sex, Latino societies

Biography
Norine Berenz' doctoral dissertation on person deixis in Brazilian Sign Language was based on three years of fieldwork, most of which she did while resident in Brazil. After completing the doctoral program at the University of California at Berkeley in 1996, she taught linguistics at the Holy Names College in Oakland, California, at the University of the Witwatersrand in Johannesburg, South Africa (1997–2000), where she also did some work on South African Sign Language, and at Inter American University of Puerto Rico, San German campus (2000–present).

This is not a scholarly treatise but rather an acknowledgment of the contribution to our understanding of Brazilian Sign Language (LSB) made by two Deaf Brazilian men who died of HIV/AIDS in 1995 and a commemoration of an American interpreter whose efforts to spread the word about safe Gay sex may have prevented additional, unnecessary deaths in the Brazilian Deaf community. As a linguist doing research on LSB from the mid-1980s through the mid-1990s, I had a view of the intersection of Gayness and Deafness (taking both of these from a cultural perspective) in Brazil. It is that view – an admittedly limited view – that I draw on here.

There are some similarities between Deaf societies and Latino societies in their attitude to homosexuality, if I can generalize from my own experience with the two groups (in the U.S., Puerto Rico, Brazil, and South Africa). Both tend to accept their Gay members, as long as such members' Gayness remains in the background, a kind of don't-ask-don't-tell policy. In comparison to aggressively homophobic societies, there is much to applaud in this attitude, yet silence on matters of sexuality became a contributing factor to the spread of HIV/AIDS in both Deaf and Latino societies.

In Brazil, many Gay men who marry women hide their Gayness from their wives and from the rest of their family. Often the family first learns that a member is Gay when he contracts AIDS. Sometimes a wife learns that her husband is Gay only when she herself contracts AIDS through conjugal sex. A second typical scenario is one in which everyone knows that a man sleeps with other men, but if he fulfills society's expectations by marrying a woman, fathering children, and being discreet about his homosexual "dalliances", he is accepted in heterosexual society. In general in Brazil, sexual identity is more fluid than it is in the United States. For example, cross-dressing by putatively heterosexual men is traditional in certain cultural celebrations. However, I have heard personal coming-out stories where a Gay man is ostracized by his family when he attempts to claim an overtly homosexual social identity.

Deaf Brazilians seemed to share this laissez-faire attitude. I knew Deaf men whose wives didn't know about their husbands' male sexual partners, Deaf men who were known to be bisexual, and single Deaf men whose families didn't know that they were Gay. Although there was no clear boundary between Gay and straight Deaf, there was a Deaf club in Rio de Janeiro that catered to a predominantly Gay clientele, so to that extent there was a Gay subculture in the Deaf community.

Brazilian Gay Deaf men I worked with or knew socially seemed to be Deaf first and Gay second. To the extent that they engaged in social identity politics, they focused on Deaf rights, not Gay rights: protesting discrimination against Deaf people in housing, education, and employment; seeking recognition of LSB as the primary language of members of the Deaf community, advocating for the use of LSB as medium of instruction for Deaf students, and demanding LSB-Portuguese interpreting services in government facilities. Deaf activists found a legal basis for demanding their linguistic rights in the Brazilian constitution's treatment of non-Portuguese speaking indigenous peoples, and they found a model for peaceful activism in the Gallaudet University's *Deaf President Now* protest.

Neither Roberto Robson or José Roberto Cruz stand out in my mind as Deaf activists because they were not among the most visible organizers of Deaf rights activities; yet each of them played an important role in creating the political consciousness that led Deaf Brazilians to begin to see themselves as members of a cultural and linguistic subgroup within the larger Brazilian polity.

Roberto Robson was an audiologically hard-of-hearing man born into a hearing family in Rio de Janeiro. He was educated in schools for deaf children, where he acquired LSB from his signing classmates. He also acquired a disdain for signing from his hearing teachers whose negative comments he frequently overheard. Although he was an excellent signer, he held a negative attitude to signing into his young adulthood. In fact, he would deride his LSB-dominant Deaf peers for their poor Portuguese skills. In the late 1980s he became affiliated with FENEIS, a Rio-based Deaf advocacy agency. When FENEIS began offering sign language classes, Roberto was one of the first teachers to be recruited.

Despite having held anti-signing beliefs, Roberto was unique in the early days for bringing a 'deep' variety of signing into the classroom. That is, other teachers, whether they were Portuguese-dominant or LSB-dominant, preferred to teach a variety of signing at the signed Portuguese end of the sign language variety continuum. Not so in Roberto's classroom. Roberto was also instrumental in recruiting other Deaf teachers for the FENEIS program, and video-recordings of his signing contributed data for linguistic analysis of LSB.

José Roberto Cruz was a second generation Deaf man from São Paulo. He was the LSB teacher of and consultant to Dr. Lucinda Ferreira Brito, the first linguist to do extensive research and scholarly writing on LSB (which she labeled Lingua de Sinais dos Centros Urbanos do Brasil: LSCB). When

Lucinda moved from São Paulo to the Universidade Federal de Pernambuco in Recife in the northeast of Brazil in 1985, José Roberto joined her there from time to time to continue their collaboration. His presence was a catalyst for other Deaf people to become involved in sign language teaching and research. Later when Lucinda moved to the Universidade Federal do Rio de Janeiro (UFRJ), she arranged for José Roberto to be hired to teach sign languages classes. These were the first sign languages classes to be offered at a Brazilian university. Together they developed the first sign language pedagogical materials.

Both Roberto Robson and José Roberto Cruz died in 1995 from complications of AIDS.

In September 1993 Lucinda and Tania Amara Felipe (then a doctoral student doing LSB research for her dissertation) organized an international conference on sign languages at UFRJ. I contacted Nancy Frishberg to provide interpreting services, and Nancy contacted John McBride, a highly-regarded ASL interpreter who was living and working in San Francisco, California. The technical excellence and professionalism they brought to a very complex linguistic situation was a model for Brazilians, many of whom – both Deaf and hearing – worked within a paternalistic "helper" paradigm.

John, who was HIV+ and an AIDS counselor, brought a safe Gay sex video entitled "Hot and Safe." The narrator of the video signed ASL and there were English subtitles. Few Deaf Brazilians read Portuguese well, let alone English, and some could not understand ASL (although LSB and ASL are both descendants of Old French Sign Language), but all could obtain crucially important information because the video was visually explicit. Although I don't know whether a number of projects to translate the ASL to LSB and the English to Portuguese were completed, the video had a lasting impact because it broke the barrier of silence around Gay sex.

John became lovers with a very dynamic Gay Deaf man named Nelson Pimenta. Only a year or so earlier (1992), Nelson had had an epiphany when he began attending UFRJ sign language classes, being taught by Myrna Monteiro, José Roberto's replacement after José Roberto returned to São Paulo. (It was very common for other Deaf people to show up at sign language classes to observe teaching practices or just to socialize.) I first met

Nelson in 1992, when I spent eight months in Brazil doing research. Then I went back to the U.S. for six months. When I returned to Brazil in mid-1993, Nelson had changed dramatically. He had developed a confidence born of the validation he found in Lucinda's arguments for the linguistic status of LSB as a real language comparable to Portuguese, not mere "mímica", as signing was commonly called at that time.

After John returned to California, he invited Nelson to visit him there. Nelson's month-long visit in early 1994, which included observation of teaching practices at California School for the Deaf in Fremont and discussions with knowledgeable and influential Deaf Americans such as Ella Lentz and Lon Kuntze, provided him with a wealth of information and a world of new ideas. Back in Brazil, Nelson kept up an email correspondence with John until John's health status deteriorated. However, when Nelson returned to California for a year-long stay beginning in March, 1995, John again played a major part in supporting Nelson's work. When Nelson moved to Washington, D.C. for the period August to November, John joined him and introduced him to Clayton Valli, whose apartment they rented, as well as to other Deaf Americans who generously shared their ideas and experience.

John made two more trips to Brazil at his own expense, where he gave safe sex workshops to Deaf people. By the time he was preparing for his second trip in the summer of 1996, his health was deteriorating. His doctor advised him strongly that the trip would be too taxing for his severely compromised immune system. Before he left, John recounted to me his doctor's anxious foreboding. "He's warned me that I could catch something there and die!" he laughed. When John did die in February, 1997, he could rest in the peace of knowing that his information and his example had broken the silence about safe Gay sex for at least some members of the Brazilian Deaf community, so that other Gay Deaf men would be spared the suffering and early death that took Roberto Robson and José Roberto Cruz.

Contact information
Norine Berenz, Ph.D.
P.O. Box 5100, caja 31
San German, PR 00683
email: berenz@sg.inter.edu

A program for preventing sexually transmitted diseases for Deaf people in the city of São Vicente, São Paulo, Brazil

Ilham El Maerrawi

Deaf Worlds
2006 | vol 22 (1)
Forest Books ©
ISSN 1362–3125

Key words

HIV/AIDS, deafness, STDs, Brazil, multiplying agents, sexual education.

Introduction

Even though the STD/AIDS Municipal Program of São Vicente, in the state of São Paulo, Brazil, has experience in developing prevention programs for STD/AIDS, it faced a number of challenges when it was asked to create specific prevention materials for deaf people. This venture emerged from interactions between a group of interpreters and deaf people and the coordinator of the program. It was also supported by the Municipal Chamber of São Vicente, attending to the needs of the deaf population and people who work and/or live with them.

By accepting these challenges, we not only wanted to create graphic material, but also structure a project of prevention for deaf people. This work was an expansion of previous work with groups such as confined people, drug addicted people, gays, homosexuals, prostitutes, women and adolescents, among others. We had also been developing informative and useful educational material for the community at large.

After months of research with professionals who work with the deaf community, sites and departments related to the assistance of people with special needs, we found that there was a general lack of specific prevention materials and projects for the deaf population. We identified only two non-governmental organizations that had developed a manual with text and pictures for the deaf population in other states. We also found out that São Vicente has more than 4,000 deaf people and that the majority are illiterate and excluded from the society. The community is sexually quite active but according to reports there is a great lack of information about STD prevention as well as on how to use of condoms.

Because of the lack of materials and projects addressing the deaf population's needs, we are doing basic research with deaf people, interpreters and local associations so that we can develop material that uses sign language to convey the necessary AIDS prevention information for deaf and illiterate people.

Our project

The goal of our project is to inform deaf people about HIV/AIDS, aiming at the prevention of sexually transmitted diseases and providing access to reference service centers. We started with several meetings to decide on the necessary content. We wanted to provide condensed but clear and direct information. We also wanted to define the appropriate signs, since each region has its own dialect with its own characteristic signs.

The next step was to find and hire a communications agency that had experience in this area or that was willing to overcome the obstacles. A team of STD/AIDS professionals, a professional interpreter and two literate deaf people who are also interpreters, produced the folders. The material they developed contains simple information about STD/AIDS contamination through sexual intercourse, drug addiction and breastfeeding, and the ways of prevention. It also emphasizes the use of condoms. The deaf people on the project volunteered to be the photographic models for the folder.

The prevention project

We trained deaf and hearing people to become "multiplying agents" using the pairs education methodology and developed ways to educate deaf people at the places they are most likely to congregate. Several partnerships were established – with Deaf associations, non-governmental organizations, and supporting groups for deaf people – so that our STD/AIDS/Hepatitis training workshops could be done.

In those training workshops, the focus was on STDs, HIV/AIDS and hepatitis, including ways of contamination and possibilities of prevention. The workshops included a safe sex information, how to reduce the harm of injected and non-injected injection drugs, ethics, prejudice, vulnerability, advice for people with STD/AIDS, and training in the specific practices of the multiplying agents. The workshops also dealt with how to create comprehensible materials for deaf people and what signs are compatible with the target group. Out of 15 people who participated in the workshop, only three felt secure enough to become multiplying agents. The others became supporters of the project.

The education portion of the project was then carried out in places where deaf people usually meet, such as public squares, bars, parties, at beach soccer games, sports championships for deaf people, and along the beaches during the night. Besides this field work, it was also necessary to re-structure the referral services to STD/AIDS treatment centers, particularly the Test and Advice Center (CTA) since there was an alternative prevention program with interpreters there, and the specialized assistance service (SAE). One measure was to make sure that referral centers had appointments and interpreters available for deaf people.

There were many difficulties in the production of our information folder. One of them was to define what was the most important information and what was the best way to transmit it clearly to deaf people. Another difficulty was the different dialects used by deaf people. We were concerned that the material should not be too long or too confusing. For all these reasons, we needed a way of presenting these messages in a way that was concise but effective.

The use of signs and photographs was essential. The training of deaf multiplying agents demanded a total reformulation of our STD/AIDS program. We had to carefully examine our presentations and all the techniques and language resources we used for the best way to assist deaf and illiterate people. During the workshops, we observed an immense interest by the deaf participants in having safer sexual relationships but also the great lack of information about sexuality, prevention, contraceptives, the use of condoms and about testing and assisting services to STD/AIDS/Hepatitis.

Our successes

We have reached deaf people in the places they frequent most often, such as beaches, public squares and bars, particularly on the weekends. During the week, we gave lectures in schools. The deaf multiplying agent Mônica, the interpreter Dany and the STD/AIDS program professionals created a partnership with the Secretariat of Education to give the lectures in classes where there were deaf students. The most important objective was to publish the project, to inform deaf people about it, and to set up the CTA as referral service for deaf people, where they could acquire information, obtain condoms and take HIV, syphilis and hepatitis tests. Tuesday was designated as the day for deaf people. The multiplying agent also met and accompanied people to the CTA. In a six-month period, there were 49 interventions and 483 orientations. In addition, 1,115 condoms handed were out during this period, a significant number since most of the deaf people reported that they had never used condoms before.

Proposals for the future

To further improve our these services, the professionals of the program will be trained in sign language (LIBRA) so that they have at least a minimum knowledge about this kind of communication and can convey prevention information using sign language. Deaf multiplying agents also need to be supported in their role as health promoters, helping them spread the information about STD/AIDS prevention to all deaf people. At this time, the local Secretariat of Health has expanded the project to drug addicted deaf people who have demanded an appropriate strategy for this population and the guarantee of a multiplying agent for their community.

The barriers of prejudice, communication problems and poor education makes deaf people in São Vicente extremely vulnerable to HIV. In many situations, deaf people were dismayed by our work but it became something interesting and entertaining. In the end, our work did raise consciousness about prevention among deaf people. The structure of the CTA as a health service center was important to the acceptance of this work and for spreading information about prevention measures, HIV testing, orientations, informative material and the use of condoms in the deaf community.

Program details and contact information
Municipal City Hall of São Vicente
Secretariat of Health
STD/AIDS/Hepatitis Program of São Vicente
Coordinator: Ilham El Maerrawi
Multiplying Agent: Mônica Tintore de Araujo
Volunteer: Deny-ILS and City Chamber member: Gilberto Rampon
Secreatriat Staff: Valéria Zuniga, Samantha Theodosio, Marco Antonio de Oliveira, Rosana Bárrio, Regina Andreazzi, Paula J. Araujo, Glaucia Francatto
email: dstaids@saudesaovicente.sp.gov.br

HIV/AIDS and Deafness in Flanders

Isabelle Heyerick for Fevlado, with additional information from SENSOA

Deaf Worlds
2006 | vol 22 (1)
Forest Books ©
ISSN 1362–3125

Key words

Flemish Deaf community, HIV/AIDS, textphone, counseling, Flanders.

Biography

Isabelle Heyerick has an M.A. in Germanic languages and is a sign language interpreter. She works with Fevlado, lobbying for equal rights and chances for Deaf people in every domain of life.

Introduction

Flanders is the Flemish speaking part of Belgium. As far as we, the Federation of Flemish Deaf Organisations (Fevlado) are informed, HIV and/or AIDS does not pose a problem in the Deaf community. However it is not 100% clear if this means that there are no problems or that they are not reported to the Federation. We also do not have any specific information about whether the actual risk of contagion is higher with Deaf people than with hearing people.

The problem Deaf people have as opposed to hearing people is that it is not easy for them to get informed about HIV and AIDS. All campaigns are directed at hearing people, using media which are not accessible to deaf people: spoken language commercials on TV, information brochures written in language that is too difficult to understand, and TV shows which have no subtitles or sign language interpreters. There was in the past, however, an unsuccessful initiative to provide information about HIV and AIDS by text telephone.

The AIDS phone

In Flanders, the government through SENSOA, a governmental body responsible for creating public awareness related to sexuality and its risks, organised an initiative called the AIDS Phone. This was a free telephone number where Flemish people who had questions about HIV and AIDS could talk with experts who would inform them. In the beginning, this service was not accessible for deaf and hard of hearing persons. Starting in March 1996, the AIDS Phone service was equipped with a text telephone. Every volunteer working for this service was trained to communicate in this way with deaf and hard of hearing people. They were taught to use short sentences, clear language and learned about the cultural background of the deaf community. This training proved to be essential.

Within the Foundation Aids Healthcare (Stichting AIDS Gezondheidszorg (StAG) in Flemish) there was an ad hoc commission *Deaf* consisting of persons from within the deaf community. These were: two deaf representatives from the Federation of the Flemish Deaf (Fevlado) and Culture for the Deaf, one deaf volunteer, two interpreters for the deaf, and one representative from the deaf schools. Further there were representatives from the service AIDS phone: two team members and two volunteers who knew sign language. During 1996, the AIDS phone received 10–20 calls from deaf and hard of hearing persons.

Until the end of 1997, the AIDS Phone for deaf and hard of hearing people was widely publicized and was promoted through ads in magazines for the deaf and information sessions during events for the deaf. In the same year, research was carried out in order to determine if the AIDS phone was known to the deaf public and if it was needed. This research showed that the deaf public did know about the phone and thought it was useful.

However, despite these results, deaf and hard of hearing people did not use the AIDS (text) telephone. The commission *Deaf* tried to promote the service, but the text telephones stayed unused during the years. During 1997 the text telephone was contacted three times and there were four questions from deaf people by fax. In 1998 the AIDS phone was contacted one time by a deaf/hard of hearing person. In 1999, the management decided to remove the text telephones. Currently, deaf and hard of hearing people can contact the AIDS Phone service by fax and email.

In an internal report of the work group about the AIDS Phone in 1999, it was stated that the deaf community has a lot of reserve in communicating about AIDS, HIV and safe sex. There were plans to adapt the book *AIDS 100 questions and answers* for deaf and hard of hearing people and to publish these in magazines for the deaf. However, the editorial offices of these magazines judged the matter was too delicate and they were never published.

Fevlado has no apparent explanation why the AIDS phone for deaf has not been successful. One of the reasons could be the mode of communication, text telephones. In Flanders, the use of text telephones has diminished over the years and they are no longer produced and sold here. As the written form of Dutch is a second language for the prelingually deaf and not their favored mode of communication, which is Flemish Sign Language, it might be that it was too difficult for some deaf people to contact the service.

Conclusion

We need more information about HIV/AIDS in the Flemish Deaf community. We currently have no way of determining if HIV/AIDS poses a real danger in the Deaf community. If we did a study on this, the information could be analyzed and, depending on the outcome, the right measures could be taken. The right information has to be given to the Deaf community about what AIDS is and this information needs to be accessible and understandable.

Contact information

Fevlado vzw
Coupure Rechts 314
9000 Gent
email: info@fevlado.be

Living partial truths: HIV/AIDS in the Japanese deaf world

Steven C. Fedorowicz

Deaf Worlds
2006 | vol 22 (1)
Forest Books ©
ISSN 1362–3125

Key words

HIV/AIDS, deafness, Japan, Japanese Sign Language, sexual education, ethnography.

Abstract

This paper is intended to be a report on the HIV/AIDS situation among Japanese deaf people. The question of whether HIV/AIDS is a problem for Japanese deaf people as it is for deaf people in other societies will be explored from a number of different angles. First, I give an overview of deafness in Japan. Second, the general HIV/AIDS situation will be described as it impacts deaf people and the mainstream society at large. Third, attempts at HIV/AIDS education in the areas of general information and prevention in Japan will be investigated, including how hearing and deaf school children learn about HIV/AIDS. Finally, I present data on the relationship between deaf people and HIV/AIDS. The heuristic device of "partial truths" will be employed in both the ethnographic and literal sense of the term. Although ways to measure incidence vary, one estimate I make is that there are approximately 300 Japanese deaf people with HIV/AIDS. Although the number might seem small, no happy ending or convenient conclusions are offered and the conclusion argues for continuing dialogue and research.

Biography

Steven C. Fedorowicz was born in Superior, Wisconsin, U.S. in 1967, received his B.A. in Social Science-International Studies and Anthropology from Michigan State University in 1990 and his M.A. in Anthropology from Washington State University in 1996. His M.A. research was on social organization and performance genres in Bali, Indonesia. In 2002, he received his Ph.D. in Anthropology from Washington State University (Ph.D. dissertation title: *An Ethnographic Examination of Deaf Culture and Sign Language in Japan*). Fedorowicz has lived in Osaka, Japan for eight years and is currently an Associate Professor of Anthropology in the Asian Studies Program at Kansai Gaidai University.

Introduction: Partial truths

For quite a long time, AIDS information has permeated among deaf people, although such information is quite wrong and distorted. I wonder about this point. (Japanese deaf informant, May 2005)

When I started to do research on deaf people in Japan with HIV/AIDS, James Clifford's notion of "partial truths" (1986) immediately came to mind. As in all research, insider and outsider perspectives, biases, omissions and mistakes all lead to gaps. Trying to fill gaps in turn reveals new gaps of knowledge. Ethnography is at best a piecing together of "fragments of discourse" (Tyler, 1986, p. 125). But in a simpler and quite literal sense, the situation surrounding HIV/AIDS in Japan for deaf and hearing people is a series of partial truths constructed and presented so that facts/statistics/ideas/opinions are often distorted or even wrong (in the scientific sense). Cullinane discusses biomedical explanations of disease as partial truths produced through various political, historical and societal pressures (2004, p. 14). Denial of a domestic problem; questionable medical business practices; laying blame upon foreigners, homosexuals, and an increasing promiscuous youth culture; massaging numbers and statistics; refusal to share diagnoses; refusal to treat infected patients; stigma and discrimination; hesitation to "come out" in society; pseudonyms and anonymous peer support groups; a lack of any clear cut government strategy; conservative views of sex education for school children; misunderstanding about disabled people's sexuality and a lack of basic information in Japanese and other languages on prevention and treatment are only a few of the pieces of the puzzle that combine and contradict to create the partial truths of HIV/AIDS in Japan. Throughout the course of this paper, these puzzle pieces will be explored, especially in relation to deaf people.

This paper is intended to be a report on the situation of Japanese deaf people with HIV/AIDS. As far as I know, there are no statistics or even an educated guess on the number of deaf people infected with HIV/AIDS in Japan. While I have been researching deaf culture and sign language in Japan for over eight years, I have never met an HIV positive deaf person, at least to my knowledge. For a group that is generally well known for being straightforward in discussions on most subjects (sometimes painfully so), Japanese deaf people are strangely quiet on this issue. This, of course, begs the question: is HIV/AIDS a problem for deaf people in Japan as it is for deaf people in other societies?

This report will address and explore this question. First, an overview of deafness in Japan will be presented. Second, the general HIV/AIDS situation will be described as it impacts deaf people as well as the mainstream society at large. Third, attempts at HIV/AIDS education in the areas of general information and prevention in Japan will be investigated. How is Japan teaching sex education to its schoolchildren and how are deaf schools teaching about HIV/AIDS? Finally, data on the relationship between deaf people and HIV/AIDS will be presented.

The theme of partial truths will run throughout this paper. The partialness of information also impacted the methodologies that were used. As of this writing, research for this report was conducted for a one-month period in May, 2005. A two-pronged approach was attempted, getting information about HIV/AIDS through the deaf world and then getting information about the deaf situation through the HIV/AIDS world. I conducted interviews and discussions with approximately 30 deaf individuals in Japanese Sign Language, examined available literature in Japanese and English, utilized internet sources and bulletin boards and corresponded with many organizations and groups. All written correspondence was carried out in Japanese and then translated into English by a native Japanese professional translator. For various reasons, actual face-to-face contact and participant-observation were not utilized as much as this author would have liked.

My previous work (Fedorowicz, 2002) has been an attempt to provide cultural descriptions of deaf people in Japan from an outsider's point of view. This sort of representation is problematic in the sense that it is the anthropologist who decides what information and whose voices to include in a written text. I have tried to deal with this problem through various writing techniques but still must concede that "even the best ethnographic texts – serious, true fictions – are systems, or economies, of truth. Power and history work through them, in ways their authors cannot fully control" (Clifford, 1986, p. 7). More recently Kuwayama discusses this issue in his treatise on native anthropologists: "Representation is political, at least potentially, because it is unclear who describes whom or acts for whom, and for what purpose" (2004, p. 16). How will an anthropological text, especially on an extremely sensitive issue, be used and by whom? This is not only the concern of the author, but, as Kuwayama reminds us, the concern of those who are being written about. Natives[2] read what is written and produced about them and have the ability to critique and protest. This process also happens during the course of ethnographic fieldwork. Natives decide how and if they want to be informants or collaborators. They decide what information to provide and in what form. HIV/AIDS tends to be a very private and secretive issue in Japan. Anthropological motives are not spared from suspicion. While gathering data, especially qualitative data, I have been denied contact by some people and asked to keep information confidential by others. As frustrating as it is when an informant gives valuable information and then requests that it be kept private, such requests must be honored. And so, for better or for worse, this report contributes to partial truths.

The deaf world in Japan is rather small and gossip seems to fly at lightning speed at times (especially with the internet and cellular phone email). Seemingly insignificant details might identify a deaf person and precautions are taken to prevent such an occurrence. Thus, in this paper, all informants and people who have shared information will be presented as anonymous. The same holds true for certain peer support groups as well. Sensitive information received will be paraphrased and certain details modified to protect the privacy of individuals. Still, with taking such precautions, it is acknowledged that "[r]esearch by outsiders sometimes upsets natives because it lays bare the cultural unconscious, which has been buried in the mind in the process of socialization, thus provoking collective anxiety and discomfort" (Kuwayama, 2004, p. 20). It has been my hope that I have minimized anxiety and discomfort in this sense so that this important issue can be discussed in a format and setting that is acceptable by all involved. Most (but not all) of the deaf individuals I contacted for assistance and information seemed interested in this issue and expressed a desire to learn more. The partial truths collected, explored and presented in this paper are intended in spirit as part of a "forum for dialogue" in the sense of an "open text" (Kuwayama, 2004, p. 45) rather than any sort of conclusion or closure.

The Japanese deaf world

Out of a total population of approximately 127.4 million, there are an estimated 346,000 hearing impaired adults and 15,200 hearing impaired children recognized by the Japanese government (Prime Minister's Office, 2004, pp. 121, 126). These are people who have registered as *shougaisha* ("handicapped/disabled people") in their local communities and carry a special handicap notebook that serves as identification. This notebook lists the individual's so-called disability as well as a ranking of severity, which in turn determines the amount and type of social welfare assistance the individual is allowed to access. These figures do not include thousands of individuals who have lost hearing due to old age. As I am interested in deaf people who use sign language as a primary means of communication and who participate in deaf organizations and activities, elderly people who do not meet these criteria are not within the scope of this research.

The following descriptions of Japanese deaf people come primarily from research conducted for my dissertation (Fedorowicz, 2002) which entailed three years of fieldwork in the Kansai area (Osaka, Kyoto, Nara) of Japan. Methods included participant-observation in various deaf groups and sign language circles, analyses of media and deaf entertainment, written questionnaires and interviews conducted in Japanese Sign Language.

In academic and social welfare settings in the U.S. and Europe, deafness is usually thought of in terms of deficiency or cultural belonging. Deficit models treat deafness as a disability, abnormality and something to be cured/overcome. Cultural models treat deaf people as a somewhat unified group and/or linguistic minority. These models are relevant in Japan on some levels. However, ethnographic data questions any single model explaining the daily life and realities faced by Japanese deaf people. Varieties of deafness and personal circumstances are important in an individual's self-identity. Some people are born deaf, others lose hearing later in life, some are hard of hearing and some are so-called multiply handicapped (deaf-blind and deaf with cerebral palsy for example). Deaf individuals often refer to themselves as being "disabled" or belonging to "deaf culture" (or both) depending upon their personal background, particular circumstances and style of communication.

An important question is "Is there a 'deaf culture' in Japan?" Lane et al. (1996, pp. 71, 159) suggest four criteria for treating the American Deaf as a minority (thus implying a cultural group): 1) shared physical or cultural characteristics (i.e. deafness and the use of a common language, American Sign Language), 2) shared identity, 3) endogamous marriage (the American Deaf are reported to inter-marry 90% of the time), and 4) shared oppression. Decisions and policies are made (or more often are not made) for deaf people with very little deaf participation.

Can the Lane et al. model be applied to Japan? The Japanese deaf share the physical characteristic of deafness and use sign language. The use of sign language[3] is usually cited as the most important characteristic of deaf people in Japan. As far as marriage goes, most of my deaf informants who are married have a deaf spouse. Single deaf people usually express a desire to marry another deaf person.

Shared oppression is also present among deaf people of Japan. This oppression includes insufficient access to information and inability to obtain certain jobs (and higher salaries). Examples of the former include a lack of captions on television, especially during emergency situations, not being able to hear announcements at train stations and other public locations and an over-reliance upon the telephone by hearing people. Deaf people are often frustrated by a lack of fax machines at stores and other public service locations.[4] Also, there is a shortage of sign language interpreters, especially competent ones, because they usually work as volunteers or receive very small payments. As for deaf employment, there are many restrictions, both legal and logistical, that do not allow deaf people to hold certain jobs. There are at least 300 legal restrictions that effect handicapped people in general (Zenkoku Choukaku Shougaisha Renraku Kaigi, 2000); deaf people legally cannot become doctors, nurses, pharmacists, dentists, police officers, pilots, etc. Many of these restrictions have been in place since the Meiji era (1868–1912). While these restrictions are slowly being re-examined and changed, the process is not seen as rapid enough (Ishinado no menkyo …, 2001, A-3).

Shared identity is the challenging element of this model. There is much variation among Japanese deaf people, and it would probably be too simplistic to say that there is one unified deaf culture (in Japan, or any other society for that matter). However, I have outlined four major deaf themes in Japan as identified in daily life settings and deaf cultural performances that indicate some kind of shared identity. To summarize (more detail can be found in Fedorowicz, 2002, pp. 103-106), the themes include:

The challenge of communication. Deaf people navigate within a predominantly hearing society that does not know sign language, hampering them both in face-to-face interactions with most hearing people as well as when using non-face-to-face technologies such as telephones that depend on speech and hearing. Writing faxes and sending emails are not practical means of reporting life-threatening incidents or requesting emergency services from the police, fire departments and medical personnel.

Sign language opens the world. Japanese society and the deaf education system place great emphasis on speech. Despite this, deaf people learn sign language, use it among themselves, and express joy at being able to fully express themselves and have others fully understand them.

The challenge of misunderstanding. When deaf people navigate in the hearing world, they often have to deal with simple *faux pas* of uninformed hearing people. Deaf inspired television dramas[5], despite their limitations, express this theme over and over again. Changes in society that deaf people desire often include more and better interpreters, captions on television, access to timely emergency information and other "barrier free" issues. But the most common desire is for more understanding about deaf people and the recognition of JSL as their native language.

Creating a positive image. The desire to create a positive image, either along the lines of Deaf Pride or through merely living life to the best of one's ability, results in a representation of "deaf culture" either intentionally or not. As the majority of hearing people most likely do not have much contact with deaf people, any interaction they might encounter with deaf people will undoubtedly stick in their minds and become an interpretant of "deaf." For example, one informant responded in writing to my questionnaire:

> *In my local area there is one person who is very active and who has got a lot of vitality. And he is deaf, so he has been working hard to educate people about sign language and various [deaf] activities... Little by little the south neighborhood is becoming a better place to live.*

This informant respects the actions of her deaf neighbor (and even seems a little envious of him) who actively works at creating a positive image. Deaf people do not want to be pitied or looked down upon. They want to be recognized for what their talent and abilities, the same as everyone else.

These themes will be brought up again later in this text, but first it would be useful to discuss the general situation of HIV/AIDS in Japan as it seems to be different from other societies in many regards. A familiarity of this situation is important for understanding how HIV/AIDS affects deaf people.

HIV/AIDS in Japan

Until recently, HIV/AIDS has not been seen as a serious problem in Japan. But this is changing. Rates of HIV/AIDS infections are rising in Japan, as opposed to most other developed high-income countries. Often-cited reasons for the rising level include a perceived increase in the promiscuity of Japanese youth, declining condom use among gay men and heterosexual couples, globalization (i.e. increased movement across national boarders), an overall lack of awareness (leading to risky sexual behavior and late HIV testing) and inadequate counseling. Of course the situation is much more complex. In the following brief summary of the current HIV/AIDS situation in Japan, I borrow heavily from two current sources. The nongovernmental organization (NGO) Japan Center for International Exchange (JCIE) provides a concise report on "Japan's Response to the Spread of HIV/AIDS" (2004). Anthropologist Joanne Cullinane offers greater ethnographic detail and theoretical insight on people with HIV/AIDS in her dissertation, "Domesticating AIDS: Illness, Identity, and Stigma in Contemporary Japan" (2004).

There is a great sense of stigma regarding HIV/AIDS in Japan that often leads to discrimination. People have been denied employment, fired from their jobs, had applications for daycare for their children rejected, and refused medical and dental treatment because of their HIV status. As the family is the primary social unit in Japan, HIV/AIDS cannot be seen as an individual concern; what affects one person affects her/his family as well. Oftentimes to avoid shame, individuals with HIV/AIDS do not disclose their status to friends, associates and even family members. "Coming out" and declaring one's HIV status in the public is very rare. HIV/AIDS in Japan is acknowledged as a private/anonymous/secret affair.

The first cases of HIV/AIDS in Japan involved hemophiliacs who took tainted blood products imported mostly from the United States in the early to mid 1980s. Pharmaceutical companies imported these products because they were much cheaper than those produced domestically, and doctors encouraged patients to use them. Over 1,400 people became infected with HIV. In a 1996 court case, the Japanese Ministry of Health and Welfare (now the Ministry of Health, Labor and Welfare), along with pharmaceutical companies, were seen as negligent in taking the necessary protective steps to protect hemophiliacs from the risks of the blood products, and victims were awarded a cash settlement as well as recognition. Until recently, most Japanese people associated HIV/AIDS in Japan with hemophiliac victims.

Sexually transmitted HIV/AIDS is the major problem now in Japan. People who have been infected in this way are thought of differently than hemophiliacs. While hemophiliacs are viewed as legitimate victims with the government largely responsible for their situation, people with sexually transmitted HIV/AIDS are seen as being responsible themselves for their infection and deserving of punishment. This has led to cycles of stigma, discrimination, anonymity, paranoia, extreme surveillance and misinformation.

Part of the problem with information about HIV/AIDS comes from statistics of those who are affected. Depending upon the source, the statistics are very different. The Joint United Nations Programme on

HIV/AIDS (UNAIDS, 2004) estimates the total number of adults and children living with HIV in Japan as of 2003 to be 12,000 (with a low estimate of 5,700 and a high estimate of 19,000). The above-mentioned JCIE (2004, p. 9) estimates the number of people living with HIV/AIDS to be 20,000. The Japanese Ministry of Health, Labor and Welfare (MHLW) reports the number of people with HIV/AIDS exceeding 10,000 in the year 2005 (Infectious Disease Surveillance Center, 2004; Japanese Foundation for AIDS Prevention, 2005; however, this number does not include the 1,434 hemophiliacs with HIV/AIDS. Cullinane reports a study she characterizes as "rather conservative" by Japanese epidemiologists that suggests infections in 1997 were very under-reported and possibly 10.2 times the official figure (Matsuyama, et al., 1999, cited in Cullinane, 2004, p. 9). Applying this study now would suggest 102,000 people with HIV/AIDS in Japan to date. Many more statistics including AIDS deaths and estimated rates of increase are available from UNAIDS and MHLW sources. No matter what the actual statistics might be, all agree that the numbers are rising and pose a serious threat to Japan.

According to JCIE (2004), the Japanese government does not have a unified strategy for dealing with HIV/AIDS. Rather policies, approaches and incentives are divided between the MHLW domestically and the Ministry of Foreign Affairs (MFA) through the Official Development Assistance (ODA) scheme internationally. There seems to be little coordination between ministries. On the international front, Japan's approach is to fight all infectious diseases (including tuberculosis, polio, malaria, parasitic diseases and more recently Severe Acute Respiratory Syndrome [SARS], avian influenza and bovine spongiform encephalopathy ["mad cow disease"]) rather than focusing on HIV/AIDS specifically. Japan's Ministry of Education, Culture, Sports, Science and Technology (MEXT) has an international interest as well. In a press release dated June 26, 2002 regarding the UNESCO's "Education for All" program, MEXT stated:

> The impact of HIV/AIDS on the teaching profession and the operations of schools must be acknowledged and addressed in national educational plans... A country's education system can perform a constructive role in equipping people to address and ultimately reverse the devastating spread of the disease... National

education plans should be comprehensive, and deal with access, equity, and quality issues, and integrating primary education into an overall education policy. (Ministry of Education, Culture, Sports, Science and Technology, 2002)

Technical assistance in providing such education abroad is advocated and promised. However, Japan does not seem to have such an educational goal domestically, as will be discussed shortly.

Domestically, most policies regarding HIV/AIDS stem from the 1996 lawsuit between the infected hemophiliacs and the Ministry of Health and Welfare. In 1997, all HIV/AIDS patients (hemophiliacs and those infected by sexual transmission) were recognized as "handicapped." In 1998, these newly handicapped people became eligible for the social welfare benefits and services that physically handicapped people receive. However to be eligible, people must register their HIV/handicapped status at their local government. This is a de facto form of surveillance and it is thought that many people opt not to register. Such people are in turn limiting their treatment options.

There are over 100 NGOs dedicated to domestic cases of HIV/AIDS in Japan. (There are also many NGOs that deal with HIV/AIDS internationally, but usually within the scope of broad health care and development.) Most of these are small, have no legal status and are run by volunteers. There is usually minimal coordination between such groups. Cullinane (2004) discusses the often secretive, anonymous and paternalistic nature of new communities/peer support groups. Most "real life" accounts of HIV/AIDS victims are published under pseudonyms allowing these people to "remain in the shadows." The internet becomes a vital tool for such groups to disseminate and control information. Privacy is paramount.

This privacy issue might not seem like such an extreme response when considering how both the Japanese government and media have treated people with HIV/AIDS. Infected people are treated as public threats rather than the infection itself: HIV positive people and AIDS patients need to be flushed out and exposed for the good of society. Risk groups are often identified rather than risky sexual behavior, and then turned into target(ed) groups. The youth, gay men (or men who have sex with men [MSM]), foreigners, migrant workers, sex workers (including foreign women who come or are "brought" to work in Japan's sex trade), clientele of the sex industry, young women and injecting drug users have at one time or another been targeted. Young people are seen as engaging in casual sex more often and with multiple partners. Gay men are not using condoms and are more likely to engage in risky sexual behavior. There are relatively few foreigners in Japan yet they are over-represented in infection statistics. Foreigners are especially problematic because of language and cultural barriers. There is a serious lack of language interpretation in the areas of testing, care and treatment (JCIE, 2004, p. 17; Cullinane 2004, p. 231 footnote). Although prostitution was made illegal in 1957, Japan still has a thriving sex trade, estimated at US$13 billion per year and growing (Kakuchi, 2003). Women in the sex trade are at risk because customers rarely use condoms. Sexually adventuresome young women (the so-called "yellow cabs"[6]) are viewed as selfish and dangerous. The same goes for teenage girls engaging in *enjo kosai* ("compensated dating" where young women "date" middle-aged men in exchange for cash and/or expensive brand name items). Injecting drug use has never been a major source of HIV/AIDS transmission in Japan. However, JCIE (2004, p. 19) suggests that fearing greater stigma and possible legal punishment, individuals contracting HIV through injecting drugs might lie and claim infection through homosexual transmission.

One might be tempted to ask, is there not anyone else left to blame? Many of these target groups have been targeted for other ills of society as well. Foreigners often get blamed for increases in crime, young women (identified as "parasite singles"[7]) have been blamed for Japan's poor economy and the youth (known as "freeters" and more recently NEETs[8]) have been blamed for the economy as well as the overall deterioration of traditional Japanese values. These groups are convenient to blame. Cullinane discusses another perspective and quotes OCCUR (the Japan Association for the Lesbian and Gay Movement):

> [M]embers of these target groups face greater obstacles than most people due to a "lack of decision-making capabilities, social discrimination, and language barriers." The authors of the commentary go on to point out, "While it is partially true that 'viruses don't discriminate,' one glance at infection rates shows that it is more proper to say 'the spread of a virus reflects a society's distortions and injustices'" (OCCUR in Cullinane, 2004, pp. 162-163).

HIV/AIDS education for hearing and deaf school children

Teaching children about HIV/AIDS in Japan is problematic and muddled together with sexual education issues. An article in the International Herald Tribune/Asahi Shimbun (Segawa, 2005) presents two ways of thinking. One idea is that liberal sexual education encourages promiscuity and casual sex among young people; thus sex education at schools should be limited. Another idea is that many parents do not want the responsibility of discussing sex with their children themselves and prefer schools to teach about sex. But because of a 1998 revision in educational guidelines, schools cannot broach many topics. One Tokyo junior high school teacher commented that he could no longer teach about sexual intercourse and fertilization in nature, let alone human beings. As for HIV/AIDS, any mention of prevention or condom use is restricted.

Another article by BBC News (Head, 2004) claims that HIV/AIDS awareness education is virtually non-existent while at the same time risky sexual behavior among youths is increasing. An 18-year-old student is quoted: "We never had much sex education at school. We were taught little about contraception, or how you catch HIV or other diseases. Teachers just don't feel comfortable talking about sex." While many teachers want to change this situation, they lament that if condom use and safe sex is discussed too much at school, conservative parents and lawmakers might stop them from teaching anything about HIV/AIDS at all.

Dealing with the sexual needs of disabled people in general is an uncomfortable subject in Japan. This topic has recently come to light in Japanese society largely due to a popular new book, *Sex Volunteer*, written by Kaori Kawai (2004). Kawai interviewed disabled people and volunteers who assist disabled people fulfill their sexual needs. "People want to avert their gaze from the reality that disabled people have sexual desires just like everybody else" (Kan, 2004:A-12). Disabled people have different challenges when it comes to sex but parents, caregivers and the general public are often overprotective and/or wish to deny/ignore the whole matter.

There is also the issue about teaching handicapped children about sex. One school for mentally disabled students in Tokyo began teaching sexual education in 1999. Parents and teachers held discussion with students and demonstrated sexual acts through hand-made puppets equipped with sexual organs. Students were also taught a song about body parts. In 2003, the Tokyo Metropolitan Government deemed these activities as improper and seized all teaching materials. Parents and teachers are fighting this decision in court (Teachers for mentally handicapped to sue over banned sex education, 2005).

How do young deaf people learn about HIV/AIDS prevention and awareness? In a conversation with two deaf women in their early 20s, I found out that one was taught about AIDS in her last year of her deaf high school and even received an HIV test. The other student indicated that absolutely nothing was taught to her about HIV/AIDS in her deaf school. These students graduated from their high schools six and five years ago, respectively.

There are 106 deaf schools in Japan. To learn more about the situation, I contacted the 34 largest schools (by student population) that taught kindergarten through high school levels. I asked, via fax, if the deaf schools taught about HIV/AIDS, how they taught, at what grade level they taught and when they starting teaching about HIV/AIDS. In total I received eight replies from eight different prefectures. I will not offer any comment about this low level of response. But even from this small number one can get an idea about the amount and quality of HIV/AIDS education deaf school children are receiving.

Seven out of the eight schools replied that they taught about HIV/AIDS. The eighth school wrote that while it does not teach about HIV/AIDS, it was asked to send two students to participate in a high school AIDS forum by (presumably the prefectoral) Health and Physical Education Department in 2004. After the forum the two students wrote letters about the program that were distributed to all students in the school.

Six schools indicated that they teach at least general information about HIV/AIDS (source of infection, risk, prevention) through teacher lectures and or health class textbooks. Two schools said that they also teach about discrimination issues. One school said that it had a "sexual education month" with lectures, videos and other student activities. One school indicated that it distributed pamphlets from its prefectoral board of education. One school said that it only displayed HIV/AIDS posters.

Four schools start teaching about HIV/AIDS specifically at the junior high school level. One of these schools indicated that it usually starts teaching this information during the first year of junior high school, but that lower level students start to learn in the third year of junior high school. Two schools said they start teaching about HIV/AIDS at the high school level.

Schools said that they had been teaching about HIV/AIDS for 18 years, 15 years, 10 years and 4 years respectively. Two schools began teaching about the subject two years ago. None of the schools said that they offered HIV tests for their students; one school explained that such tests were not done because it was the private information of individual students.

This data shows much variation in the quantity and quality of HIV/AIDS education in deaf schools in Japan. It would be reasonable to assume that there is much variation of knowledge among deaf people themselves. So for those deaf school children not getting adequate information at school, where can they get information?

In various conversations with hearing college students at my own university, many indicated that they were not satisfied with the level of HIV/AIDS education and sex education they received from junior high school and high school. Often HIV/AIDS is taken up in a morals or social studies class setting where discrimination issues are discussed. Lessons about prevention and risk factors are lacking. Many students said that they feel they learned more about sex and AIDS from *manga* (comic books), magazines and television dramas. One of my students in a paper wrote that a benefit of the large amounts of pornographic materials available in Japan was its educational content; young people can learn about sex from pornographic sources. A teacher at a deaf school told me that young deaf students might also "learn" from such problematic sources which are "not necessarily correct".

HIV/AIDS in the Japanese deaf world

I think that in Japan "the world of deaf people" is in significantly close contact with the mainstream hearing society. The other day I saw news about a village where "sign language will be used as the official language" that was being created by young deaf people in America. Something like this is almost unthinkable in Japan (at least for the time being). In Japan, I think deaf people object to the hearing society yet they are significantly dependent upon the hearing society.
(Japanese deaf informant, May 2005)

As the above quote illustrates, it can be said that deaf people are subject to the same conditions as the rest of society with regards to HIV/AIDS in Japan. According to the Japanese Federation of the Deaf (JFD)[9], HIV/AIDS has never been brought up as an issue within their organization, nor is it aware of any special workshops on prevention and awareness for deaf people. While deaf people have never been identified as a risk group or target group, they do have problems with respect to accessing information. Several deaf people I talked with thought that HIV/AIDS is a problem in the deaf community, primarily because of a lack of information and a lack of understanding about deaf people in the mainstream hearing society.

One gay deaf man I interviewed is very active in the gay community and often attends conferences and workshops on homosexual issues including HIV/AIDS. He has never attended any workshop that was for deaf people exclusively. Once he attended a conference and was able to receive an HIV test; he communicated with the doctor through writing notes. This informant did mention a workshop in Nagoya where a sign language interpreter was present. He also told me about his participation in the 10th International AIDS Conference in Yokohama in 1994; while there was no official sign language interpreter, there was an American man, competent in JSL, who was able to interpret for the few deaf people there.

As that conference was in 1994, I wondered if the interpretation situation had changed at all in the last ten years for large international conferences. The 7th International Congress on AIDS in Asia and the Pacific met in Kobe in July 2005. I contacted the organizers to inquire about sign language interpretation. While there was no official interpretation offered, or any other special accommodations for deaf people, "one personal attendant [could have been] registered free of charge for a Regular Delegate who need[ed] special assistance and care" (personal correspondence, May 20, 2005).

As for other awareness/prevention education sources for deaf people in Japan, I have heard from various sources about sign language interpreters present at a few NGO events and local government lectures. I was able to find specific information about an overnight workshop for HIV/AIDS infected people geared for foreigners living in Japan and deaf people held by an organization called K Lounge in Tokyo, affiliated with the Tokyo Metropolitan Komagome Hospital.[10]

HIV/AIDS NGOs often offer telephone support for information and counseling. Of course this is not an option for deaf people. While communication can be done through faxes, when privacy is an issue, giving out one's fax number can be problematic. Counseling by fax does not seem to be efficient. The use of sign language interpreters might be a better option, if one is willing to give up the anonymity offered by telephone services. However, some people feel awkward about using hospital interpreters for fear that they might reveal their identities to other deaf people. Privacy and anonymity are overwhelming concerns of deaf people as well as hearing people.

As mentioned previously, there seems to be no statistics on the number of Japanese deaf people with HIV/AIDS. The JFD does not keep such statistics. Nor do government sponsored organizations or departments, such as the Japanese Foundation for AIDS Prevention, the MHLW Demography and Health Statistics Department, the MHLW Disability Health Welfare Department and the MHLW Disease Control Division.[11]

While research on deaf people with HIV/AIDS in Japan seems scarce, there have been at least two presentations mentioning deaf people at international HIV/AIDS organizations. The first was a presentation by Yoshimizu et al. about "AIDS education for hearing disabled people" (Chugoku-Shikoku Regional AIDS Center, 1993). This presentation reported that while young deaf people receive HIV/AIDS information in deaf schools, older people have problems getting information. Only some local governments have provided sign language interpreters for lectures on HIV/AIDS but, according to the authors, they have not been sufficient. Further problems arise because of a lack of qualified interpreters, note takers and an overall lack of sensitivity among people who provide sex education to the disabled and deaf.

The second presentation was at the 15th International AIDS Conference in Bangkok, Thailand in July, 2004. At this conference in a session on epidemiology and prevention, Motoko Hayashi discussed her work counseling deaf people in Kenya using sign language (AIDS Prevention Information Network, Japanese Foundation for AIDS Prevention, 2004). She also remarked that there is a similar need for providing information to deaf people in Japan using sign language.

There are at least two Japanese NGOs that deal with HIV positive gay deaf people.[12] One is geared especially for HIV positive gays, and since its establishment in the late 1990s, it has held a monthly gatherings for HIV positive gay people. Its website states that a staff person who can do sign language is always present at these gathering so deaf people are welcome to attend. I contacted this NGO and received a response. However, I was asked not to share any of the information I was given.

The second NGO was established in 2005 and is for HIV positive deaf gay people. It runs a bulletin board on the internet and the administrator is an HIV positive deaf gay man. In addition to administrating the bulletin board, he promises to respond to individual's emails about doctors, hospitals and other information that might be too private to be posted. There are several warnings on the bulletin board itself, warning participants to be especially careful with details as their community is small and people could easily be identified. There is also a statement saying that while the postings are public, individuals do not necessarily wish their messages to be discussed. "As a general rule, please do not talk with others about information you obtained on the bulletin board." In the first two months of the bulletin board, there were 21 postings, 18 by the administrator himself. The content has usually been links to internet new items on HIV/AIDS issues. I contacted this NGO as well but have received no reply.

There does not seem to be any support groups for non-gay deaf HIV positive people.

Continuing dialogue and open texts

Is HIV/AIDS a problem in Japan's deaf community? It would seem that HIV/AIDS is a potential problem for most Japanese whether hearing or deaf. Several partial truths as puzzle pieces have been presented in this paper. While no grand conclusions can be drawn, some of the puzzle can be pieced together and, if nothing else, suggest new areas for inquiry.

My own massaging of numbers suggests the following statistics for the number of deaf people with HIV/AIDS in Japan. Adding together the infection rates of HIV (5.14 per 100,000 people) and AIDS (2.568 per 100,000 people) as reported by the Infectious Disease Surveillance Center of the National Institute of Infectious Diseases (2004) we get a total of 7.71

per 100,000 people. Assuming a total deaf population of 361,200 (346,000 adults and 15,200 children as reported in Prime Minister's Office (2004, pp. 121, 126), multiplying that number by 7.71 and dividing by 100,000 we get 27.85. The low estimate for deaf people with HIV/AIDS therefore is approximately 30.

If we take 27.85 and multiply it by the "conservative" 10.2 figure to compensate for under-reporting (Matsuyama, et al., 1999, cited in Cullinane, 2004, p. 9) we get 284.1. A more realistic estimate, therefore, is roughly 300 people if the spread of AIDS is similar to that in the hearing population.

These numbers do not reflect any of the special circumstances or difficulties deaf people have as opposed to hearing people. Taking this into account, the number should be higher. Also taking into consideration that in the one month period of research I have learned of nine cases of deaf people with HIV/AIDS and that I have access to a mere fraction of the total population of deaf people in Japan, I would suggest that the number is even greater. More than one deaf informant expressed a concern that regardless of the current number, it will most likely increase, especially if the present situation for deaf people does not change.

Deaf students have greater disadvantages in accessing information through their educational career than hearing students (although hearing students might not be receiving that much more information anyway). Older deaf people might have missed out on any information at all if they did not go to school or went to a school where HIV/AIDS education was only taken up a few years ago. Deaf people have similar experiences to foreigners in Japan because of language and cultural barriers. While there have been a few efforts to translate materials into foreign languages, there has been insufficient attention paid to deaf people (who are Japanese citizens). There are few competent JSL interpreters and there is much misunderstanding about deaf people in society. Informants have stated that there is a serious lack of information on treatment options, medical facilities and available social welfare assistance, especially immediately after a deaf individual finds out s/he is HIV positive. Early treatment is vital so any delay in obtaining information is serious, even life threatening. While there are support groups for gay deaf people, there does not seem to be any groups for heterosexual deaf people.

If we return to the common deaf themes outlined in section 2, the following can be suggested: Communication is especially challenging in getting accurate information about HIV/AIDS and maintaining privacy; a lack of sign language in counseling and treatment closes the world for deaf people; misunderstanding of deaf culture leads to greater discrimination, and concerns over image hamper cooperation in deaf organizations and the greater deaf community. While deaf people are often unified in many issues, HIV/AIDS does not seem to be one of them. Stigma over homosexuality and AIDS is as common in deaf people as it is in hearing people. This in turn can lead to a greater sense of isolation for a deaf individual with HIV/AIDS.

This is not a happy ending. Nor should it be, considering the state of HIV/AIDS in Japan and the rest of the world. More gaps of knowledge need to be filled and uncovered by all people involved in a more coordinated fashion. This will not be an easy process. This paper has exposed methodological problems in researching HIV/AIDS in Japan. How does one do an ethnography of people who insist upon anonymity and refuse to talk with the researcher? How does one deal with sensitive information found on the internet, a public domain, when asked not to use or discuss it? There are no easy answers to these ethical dilemmas[13]. These are challenges not only for conducting research on HIV/AIDS but for continuing dialogue and solving problems. And the dialogue must continue. My text is left open with hopes of drawing in more participants in whatever forum in which they feel comfortable. "Partial truths" as an academic heuristic device is interesting, but living the partial truths of HIV/AIDS as presented in this report is unacceptable.

Notes

1. Special thanks to Hiroko Yamagiwa for Japanese translation, research assistance and incredible support. Thank you to the two anonymous reviewers who made constructive comments and suggestions of an earlier draft. I am grateful to Leila Monaghan and Constanze Schmaling for their encouragement and assistance. I am also grateful to Karen Nakamura, as well as all the deaf people and others in Japan who provided information and help. I, of course, accept all responsibility for interpreting and presenting this report. Information, feedback, comments and critique are warmly welcomed.

2. Kuwayama (2004, pp. 17-21) uses the term *native* as a person born within a particular culture and/or a person who has been fully assimilated into a particular society. Although everyone is a native of some culture, certain tensions and power inequalities from the colonial context of the word are also intentionally implied.

3. The term sign language will be used throughout this paper unless otherwise noted. The term corresponds to the Japanese word *shuwa* which is usually translated into English as "sign language." Sign language in Japan includes two major systems and a number of pidgins in between. Japanese Sign Language (JSL) can be considered as the traditional manual signs used primarily by deaf people; it is different from spoken Japanese in terms of grammar and word order. Signed Japanese uses many of the same signs found in JSL but follows the grammar and word order of spoken Japanese. Many deaf informants have referred to JSL as the language used by and among deaf people and Signed Japanese as the language used by hearing people to communicate with deaf people. There are many other differences between JSL and Signed Japanese. In addition, regional, generational, gender and honorific differences can be found in the sign language of Japan. For more information on the diversity of sign language in Japan, see Fedorowicz (2002, pp. 46-59).

4. This statement deals more with modality rather than technology as the telephone is an instrument based upon speech and rarely an option for Japanese deaf people. Deaf people in Japan primarily use fax machines and text messaging on cellular phones to communicate in non-face-to-face situations. The internet and on-line video conferencing (on personal computers and cellular phones) are also becoming popular. There has never been any large-scale teletypewriter or relay system for deaf people in Japan.

5. There have been many Japanese TV dramas portraying deaf people starring popular actors and actresses. These dramas have received high ratings. Despite problematic interpretations and questionable representations, such dramas often cause people to become interested in sign language, even if for only a short amount of time.

6. Young Japanese women (usually in their late teens and twenties) in Japan or abroad seeking foreign lovers. This phenomenon was overly sensationalized by the Japanese media in the 1990s. See Kelsky (1994).

7. Young Japanese women and men who continue to live with their parents after becoming adults. Instead of getting married, having children and contributing to the economy, parasite singles live off their parents and spend their money on leisure and pleasure. The Japanese media has focused mainly on female parasite singles. See Yamada (1999).

8. "Freeters" are young people who in work part-time or in temporary positions to enjoy certain freedoms that they would not have working full time jobs. "NEETs" refers to a British phrase meaning people "not in employment, education or training". See Japan Echo (2005).

9. The largest national organization representing deaf people in Japan. For more information see the JFD homepage at http://www.jfd.or.jp/.

10. This workshop was sponsored by the Levi-Strauss Community Activity Promotion Fund and administered by JCIE. Retrieved May 23, 2005 from http://jcie.or.jp/levi/n99.htm

11. All of these organizations were contacted by the author; none had statistics on deaf people with HIV/AIDS in Japan.

12. Although both of these NGOs can be found on the internet, which falls under public domain, I am trying to respect their wishes for privacy. Thus I am not giving the names of the groups or their internet addresses.

13. These ethical dilemmas were recently presented and discussed an anthropological meeting/conference in Japan (see Fedorowicz, 2005).

References

AIDS Prevention Information Network, Japanese Foundation for AIDS Prevention. (2004). *15th International AIDS Conference, Bangkok, Thailand, July 11-16, 2004 – summaries.* Retrieved May 25, 2005, from http://api-net.jfap.or.jp/siryou/2004_aids_conf/repo_ C06.htm

Asia Society. (2004). *The human security challenge of HIV/AIDS and other communicable diseases: exploring effective regional and global responses.* New York: Asia Society.

Chugoku-Shikoku Regional AIDS Center. (1993). *Collection of excerpts from the 7th Japan AIDS Society for AIDS Research report, 1993, Tokyo.* Retrieved May 17, 2005, from http://www.aids-chushi.or.jp/c6/nif/153.htm

Clifford, J. (1986). Introduction: partial truths. In J. Clifford & G. E. Marcus (Eds.), *Writing Culture: The Poetics and Politics of Ethnography.* Berkeley: University of California Press. 1–26.

Cullinane, J. (2004). *Domesticating AIDS: illness, identity, and stigma in contemporary Japan.* Unpublished Ph.D. dissertation, University of Chicago.

Editorial: alarming AIDS spread. (2005, March 8). *International Herald Tribune/Asahi Shimbun.* Retrieved May 19, 2005, from http://www.asahi.com/english/opinion/TKY200503080109.html

Fedorowicz, S. C. (2005). Investigating partial truths: researching HIV/AIDS in the Japanese deaf world. Unpublished paper presented at the 8th Annual Meeting of the Anthropology of Japan in Japan. Institute of Comparative Culture, Sophia University, Tokyo, Japan.

Fedorowicz, S.C. (2002). *An ethnographic examination of deaf culture and sign language in Japan.* Unpublished Ph.D. dissertation, Washington State University.

Head, J. (2004). Japan's AIDS time bomb. *BBC News.* Retrieved May 17, 2005, from http://news.bbc.co.uk/go/pr/fr/-/1/hi/world/asia-pacific/3890689.stm

Infectious Disease Surveillance Center, National Institute of Infectious Diseases. (2004). *The 2004 Annual Report on HIV/AIDS Surveillance in Japan, the National AIDS Surveillance Committee, Ministry of Health, Labor and Welfare.* Retrieved May 25, 2005, from http://idsc.nih.go.jp/iasr/iasr-ge1.html

Ishinado no menkyo shougaishya ni mo koufu kaiseian ga seiritsu [Licenses such as doctor will be issued to disabled people, too. Revised law was concluded.]. (2001, June 23). *Yomiuri Shimbun*, A-3.

Japan Center for International Exchange. (2000). *Levi-Strauss community activity promotion fund*. Retrieved May 23, 2005, from http://jcie.or.jp/levi/n99.htm

Japan Center for International Exchange. (2004). *Japan's response to the spread of HIV/AIDS.* Tokyo: Japan Center for International Exchange.

Japanese Foundation for AIDS Prevention. (2005). *AIDS statistics in Japan as of April 3, 2005.* Retrieved May 25, 2005, from http://apinet.jfab. or.jp/mhw/survey/mhw_survey.htm

Japan's new misfits. (2005, February). *Japan Echo, 32,* 1. Retrieved May 31, 2005, from http://www.japanecho.co.jp/sum/2005/320103.html

Joint United Nations Programme on HIV/AIDS (UNAIDS). (2004). *2004 report on the global HIV/AIDS epidemic: 4th global report.* Retrieved May 25, 2005, from http://www.unaids.org/bangkok2004/GAR2004_ html/GAR2004_14_en.htm

Kakuchi, S. (2003, March 17). Japan only now confronting rising HIV rate: women in sex trade most at risk. *San Francisco Chronicle,* A-8. Retrieved May 23, 2005, from http://www.sfgate.com/cgi-bin/article.cgi?f/chronicle/archive/2003/03/17/MN76451.DTL&type-health

Kan, S. (2004, December 18). Focusing on disabled people's sexual needs. *Daily Yomiuri,* A-12.

Kawai, K. (2004). *Sekksu boranteia* [Sex volunteer]. Tokyo: Shinchosa.

Kelsky, K. (1994). Intimate ideologies: transnational theory and Japan's "yellow cabs". *Public Culture, 6 (3),* 1–14.

Kuwayama, T. (2004). *Native anthropology: the Japanese challenge to western academic hegemony.* Melbourne: Trans Pacific Press.

Lane, H., Hoffmeister, R., & Bahan, B. (1996). *A journey into the Deaf-world.* San Diego: Dawn Sign Press.

Matsuyama, Y., Hashimoto, S., Ichikawa, S., Nakamura, Y., Kidokoro, T., Umeda, T., Kamakura, M., Kimura, S., Fukutomi, K., Ikeda, C., & Kihara, M. (1999). Trends in HIV and AIDS based on HIV/AIDS surveillance data in Japan. *International Journal of Epidemiology, 28 (6),* 1149–1155.

Ministry of Education, Culture, Sports, Science and Technology. (2002, June 26). *A new focus on education for all.* Retrieved May 19, 2005, from http://www.mext.go.jp/english/news/2002/07/020702.htm#top

Prime Minister's Office. (2004). *Heiseijuuninenban shougaisha hakusho* [Year 2003 white paper on disabled people]. Tokyo: Prime Minister's Office.

Segawa, S. (2005, January 15). Information overload: sex ed: to teach or not top teach. *International Herald Tribune/Asahi Shimbun.* Retrieved May 19, 2005, from http://www.asahi.com/english/lifestyle/TKY200501150158.html

Teachers for mentally handicapped to sue over banned sex education. (2005, May 11). *Mainichi Shimbun.* Retrieved May 19, 2005, from http://mdn.mainichi.co.jp/news/20050511p2a00m0dm013000c.html

Tokyo wants to restrict youth sex. (2004, September 22). *Japan News.* Retrieved May 19, 2005, from http://ikjeld.com.japannews/00000034.php

Tyler, S. A. (1986). Post-modern ethnography: from document of the occult to occult document. In J. Clifford & G.E. Marcus (Eds.), *Writing Culture: The poetics and politics of ethnography.* Berkeley: University of California Press. 123–140.

Yamada, M. (1999). *Parasaito shinguru no jidai* [The age of parasite singles]. Tokyo: Chikuma Shinsho.

Zenkoku Choukaku Shougaisha Renraku Kaigi. (2000). *13 kai no zenkoku choukaku shougaisha renraku kaigi kouryukai* [Program to the 13th Annual Meetings of All Japan Hearing Disabled Persons' Conference].

Contact information
Steven C. Fedorowicz
Associate Professor of Anthropology
Asian Studies Program
Kansai Gaidai University
16-1 Nakamiyahigashino-cho
Hirakata-shi, Osaka 573-1001
Japan
email: gonthros@kansaigaidai.ac.jp

ARTICLE SUBMISSIONS

Authors' attention should be drawn to the following requirements for submissions.

i. Authors should submit papers in digital format, as Word, RTF, or ASCII files; illustrations should be included as separate JPEG, TIFF or EPS files at a minimum resolution of 150dpi. Files are accepted via email, or posted on 3.5" disks or on CD ROM. Please include 'quick contact' details, and clearly list all files included with your submission.

ii. Submissions must include a 200-word abstract, publishable address for correspondence, and six indexing keywords.

iii. Following the abstract, authors must also include a short biographical paragraph.

iv. All articles must include full references, and be set out *exactly* according to the following standard examples. nb: articles and chapters should carry page numbers.

Bloomfield, L. (1933) Language. New York: Holt.

Brugmann, K. (1906) Grundriss der vergleichenden Grammatik der indogermanischen Sprachen. 2nd ed., vol. 2, part 1. Strassburg: Trubner.

Chomsky, N. (1957) Syntactic structures. (Janua Linguarum 4.) The Hague: Mouton.

Davidson, D. (1980) What metaphors mean. In Platts, M. (ed.) Reference, Truth and Reality. London: Routledge & Kegan Paul. 238–254.

Fergosun, C. (1959) Diglossia. Word 15. 325-40.

Fillmore, C. J. (1971a) Verbs of judging: an exercise in semantic description. In Fillmore, C. J. & Langendoen, D. T. (eds.) Studies in Linguistic Semantics. New York: Holt, Rinehart & Winston. 273–290.

Fillmore, C. J. (1971b) Towards a theory of deixis. The PCCLLU Papers (Department of Linguistics, University of Hawaii) 3:4. 219–241.

Monheit, D. S. (1993) Review of Hatch, E. Discourse and language education. Language in Society 22:4. 581–584.

Sacks, H., Schegloff, E. A. & Jefferson, G. (1974) A simplest systematics for the organization of turn-taking in conversation. Language 50:4. 696–735.

Slobin, D. (1991) Learning to think for speaking: native language, cognition, and rhetorical style. Pragmatics 1:1. 7–26.

v. Papers will be published with a 'date of first submission' / 'date accepted' indication.

vi. Papers may be lightly edited by the editor to seek to preserve anonymity when forwarding to reviewers.

Authors should take all due precautions to avoid self-identification.

vii. The editorial team will not accept responsibility for re-writing articles to conform to international English language standards for publication in a journal of this kind. Authors must take responsibility for presenting their material appropriately, and, at the editor's discretion, submissions will not be sent out to referees until they reach a minimum common practice threshold in this respect.

viii. Authors may choose to provide an additional paragraph which presents their abstract in a language other than English (eg. for the benefit of a wider 'home' audience). Authors are responsible wholly for this non-English text.

ix. Deaf Worlds will never knowingly publish material in which the author chooses to use offensive or disabling language (appropriately citing others' language is not seen as a matter of choice in this sense).

x. It is the author's responsibility to obtain written permission to reproduce material that has appeared in another publication, including quotations, tables and illustrations, and this should be submitted with the material.

xi. Authors of articles accepted for publication will receive digital page proofs for correction (if non-digital format is required, please notify the editorial team at first submission), plus advice on marking changes. This stage must not be used as an opportunity to revise the paper, because alterations are extremely costly. Major alterations cannot be accepted; extensive changes will be charged to the author and will probably result in publication being postponed to a later issue. Speedy return of corrected proofs (i.e. within one week) is important.

xii. Authors will receive off-prints of their article, plus a copy of the full journal issue, free of charge. Additional copies may be ordered when returning corrected proofs and a scale of charges can be supplied on request.

xiii. Submissions should be sent to:
Graham H. Turner
Editor, Deaf Worlds
Languages & Intercultural Studies
School of Management & Languages
Heriot-Watt University
Edinburgh EH14 4AS
Scotland
e-mail: g.h.turner@hw.ac.uk
Tel: +44 (0)131 451 4203
Fax: +44 (0)131 451 3079